gs bam2

The Effect of Advancing Age

upon the Human Spinal Cord

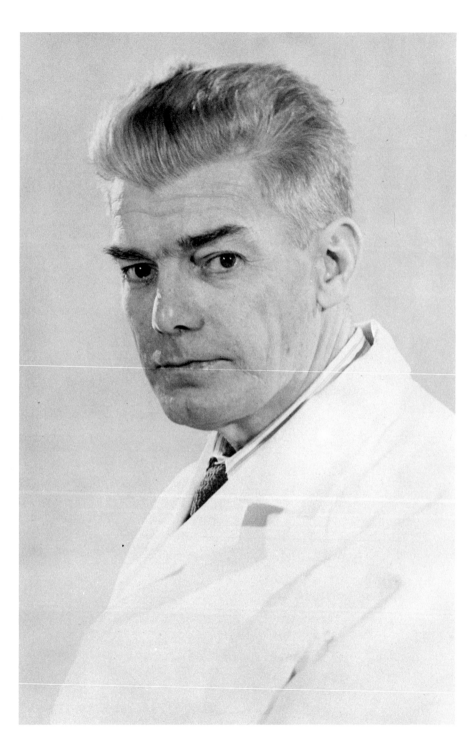

L. Raymond Morrison   1897–1950

The Effect of
Advancing Age
upon the Human
Spinal Cord

L. RAYMOND MORRISON, M.D.

with the collaboration of

STANLEY COBB, M.D.
WALTER BAUER, M.D.

Published *for* THE COMMONWEALTH FUND
by HARVARD UNIVERSITY PRESS, Cambridge, Mass., 1959

LIBRARY OF CONGRESS CATALOG CARD NO. 58-10395

MANUFACTURED IN THE UNITED STATES OF AMERICA

Published for The Commonwealth Fund
by Harvard University Press, Cambridge, Massachusetts

For approximately a quarter of a century THE COMMONWEALTH FUND, through its Division of Publications, sponsored, edited, produced, and distributed books and pamphlets germane to its purposes and operations as a philanthropic foundation. On July 1, 1951, the Fund entered into an arrangement by which HARVARD UNIVERSITY PRESS became the publisher of Commonwealth Fund books, assuming responsibility for their production and distribution. The Fund continues to sponsor and edit its books, and cooperates with the Press in all phases of manufacture and distribution.

Distributed in Great Britain by Oxford University Press, London

Preface

In 1929 a special unit for the care and study of patients with rheumatoid diseases was set up in the Medical Clinic of the Massachusetts General Hospital in Boston. On the clinical side, the program was concerned with improved therapy, and on the research side, with more comprehensive descriptions of individuals affected with rheumatic diseases, more detailed accounts of anatomical and physiological changes produced in the joints, and (somewhat later) with the chemical and physiological alterations in the connective tissue—the tissue in which the pathological changes of the rheumatic diseases are found.

A recently published volume, *Rheumatoid Arthritis: A Definition of the Disease and a Clinical Description Based on a Numerical Study of 293 Patients and Controls,** relates one aspect of our comprehensive study of rheumatoid arthritis. The patients included in this series were systematically questioned and examined in regard to clinical features in which the nervous system might have been involved. Confirmation was thus obtained of our impression that neurological manifestations form an integral part of the syndrome of rheumatoid arthritis. Histological examinations of the spinal cords of some of the patients were also undertaken in an attempt to establish the anatomical basis for the various muscular and neurological symptoms and signs that are frequently encountered in this disease. For the purpose of comparison, similar examinations were made in cases of rheumatic fever, lupus erythematosus, periarteritis nodosa, dermatomyositis, and scleroderma without pathological evidence of arthritis. It soon became apparent, however, that control material must be collected in order to show the changes which occur normally with increasing age, decade by decade. Without benefit of the latter, it was impossible to determine the specificity of the spinal cord lesions observed in rheumatoid arthritis and seemingly related diseases. Control material was therefore collected along with the pathological. The present monograph represents the results of our effort to establish a base line, or normal control, for any studies of the human spinal cord in which the factors associated with increasing age must be taken into account.

Although certain members of the arthritis study team participated in the review of the clinical records, the interpretation of the clinical findings, and the collection of spinal cords from the rheumatic disease patients and the so-called controls, Dr. L. Raymond Morrison was re-

* See footnote, page vi.

sponsible for the description and interpretation of the observed histological alterations. Though Dr. Morrison was the neuropathologist to the Psychiatric Service at this time, he soon became a most active part-time member of the arthritis study team. He had spent twelve years studying the collected material and three years working on the monograph at the time of his death in August 1950.* When an ardent and gifted investigator is suddenly cut off by death in the midst of his active career, the loss to science is immeasurable. To his family and friends, the tragedy is poignant.

We have taken up the task where Dr. Morrison left off. Fortunately, there was little to add. The illustrations were well-labeled, and the text was complete except for a few omissions, which were covered in most cases by adequate notes on file in the laboratory, and only few paragraphs had to be omitted because we were not certain of the author's meaning. On the whole, the work of completing the manuscript for publication was largely a matter of assembling the manuscript and illustrations, putting them together, and inserting the references in the right places. Editorial changes were minimal. Needless to say, it was a privilege to participate in this last collaborative work with a colleague whom we so much admired.

Although the sources of funds for the support of this care-of-the-patient and research program have been recognized in the three previous Commonwealth Fund publications,† we wish to acknowledge this generous support once again. We particularly wish to express our gratitude to the Commonwealth Fund for a large annual grant for each of the past twenty years. This continued support has enabled us to complete several long-term research projects.

It was due to the interest, encouragement, and cooperation of Dr. Frank R. Ober, Dr. James H. Means, and the late Drs. Cecil K. Drinker and S. Burt Wolbach that this research venture in the field of rheumatic diseases was finally launched. Little did we suspect, when we embarked on it in 1928, that it would lead to a study which would attempt to ascertain the effect of advancing age on the human spinal cord.

This histological study of the effect of advancing age upon the human spinal cord, initiated by one of us (W. B.) and Dr. Morrison, was aided by various past and present members of the Lovett Fund group and the

---

* An obituary, summarizing Dr. Morrison's professional life and scientific accomplishments, appeared in *Archives of Neurology and Psychiatry*, 65:788 (1951).

†Bennett, G. A., Waine, H., and Bauer, W., *Changes in the Knee Joint at Various Ages with Particular Reference to the Nature and Development of Degenerative Joint Disease*. The Commonwealth Fund, New York, 1942.

Ropes, M. W., and Bauer, W., *Synovial Fluid Changes in Joint Disease*. Published for the Commonwealth Fund by Harvard University Press, Cambridge, 1953.

Short, C. L., Bauer, W., and Reynolds, W. E., *Rheumatoid Arthritis: A Definition of the Disease and a Clinical Description Based on a Numerical Study of 293 Patients and Controls*. Published for the Commonwealth Fund by Harvard University Press, Cambridge, 1957.

Department of Pathology, Massachusetts General Hospital. Miss Margaret E. Carroll, who participated in this study from its inception, prepared the excellent histological sections and helped in many other ways. Dr. Pedro M. Catoggio of Buenos Aires, Argentina, gave valuable assistance during the three years (1946–1949) that he was a member of the group. We wish to express our gratitude to each of them. Without their help, the study would not have been possible. We wish, finally, to thank the Division of Publications of the Commonwealth Fund for their excellent editorial assistance in the preparation of this and previous manuscripts for the printer.

We hope that the present publication will not only prove useful to students of diseases of the spinal cord but will also assist others to interpret the neurological manifestations of rheumatoid arthritis and related diseases.

W. B.
S. C.

June, 1958

Contents

Summary   125

Part I

Histology

Introduction

The histology of the normal spinal cord is often complicated by pathological alterations of various kinds and degrees. While one or more of these changes might be present in a given case without causing symptoms, they must still be considered signs of disease, for a greater intensity of the same sign or a different combination of others might produce clinical effects and under those circumstances the cord would be called abnormal.

Our knowledge of the histology of the normal spinal cord must be derived from the study of the cords of healthy young adults, who die suddenly and whose life histories contain no accounts of serious illness. But such cords must be considered "ideal," for relatively few cases fulfilling this combination of requirements come to autopsy. The usual cord met with in practice is from a person of advanced years, who has suffered from more or less serious diseases and whose death followed a rather lingering illness. Even though the patient has had no recognized neurological disease, the chances are that his spinal cord will not be the same as an entirely normal spinal cord. The effects of fever or toxemia from a terminal illness may make themselves felt, certain systemic diseases like diabetes or arteriosclerosis may leave signs in the spinal cord, and (last but not least) age itself may produce alterations that would not be found in the cord of a healthy young adult. For these reasons it seemed important to study a series of run-of-mill spinal cords, as they came to autopsy in a general hospital, from persons with no neurological symptoms. Such an undertaking is useful and indeed necessary in building up control material for the study of pathological cords, especially if the lesions are not severe. The usual tendency has been to contrast supposedly pathological cords with a theoretically normal, or ideal cord. But this may lead to unjustifiable emphasis upon insignificant variations, particularly if the series of cases is small. In order to establish something like a picture of the usual, non-neuropathological, supposedly normal spinal cord, it is necessary to find how far such a cord can deviate from the ideal normal. The purpose of this investigation is to detect the alterations that occur in cords that one would naturally assume to be normal and to attempt to find some order or relationship in the intensity or frequency of the most common or most constant alterations.

The criteria by which a cord is called normal have been many years accumulating, and while some of the standards have been arrived at by specific and purposeful investigations, most of the judgments are based merely on a knowledge of general principles. Bruce's splendid *Atlas*[1] gives in clear and precise detail the number and the grouping of the nerve cells of the gray matter of the thirty-one different levels of the spinal cord. In addition to the more or less mathematical presentation of the arrangement of the nerve cells, the author also illustrates and carefully describes the configuration of the cord at its various levels, as seen in Weigert preparations. With the aid of this *Atlas* one can come pretty close to identifying sections from any level of the cord and detecting alterations in the number and distribution of the cells, as well as to recognizing the intensity and distribution of myelin. Earlier contributions were so sketchy in their presentations or so limited in their scope that no complete picture of the cord could be obtained. Of course Bruce's *Atlas* was merely topographical and none of the more refined details of structure were described or illustrated. But the normal standards for nerve cells had already been established by the work of Nissl,[2] and many other details of nerve cell classification and cytology have been added since.[3] The theory of the distribution and reaction of neuroglia in the brain that was so thoroughly developed by Cajal and his co-workers has served as the basis of many of the assumptions about glia. Some authors have questioned the accuracy of these assumptions and Jakob[4] and his pupils[5] have tried to show that the glial reactions in the cord are rather different from those in the brain. Hassin[6] goes so far as to imply that the normal spinal cord does not contain microglia. The blood supply of the cord, while fairly well understood since the investigations of Adamkiewicz[7] and Ross,[8] is still being worked out even in its grosser anatomical pathology. The meninges like all other structures of the cord have been studied in great detail in all sorts of pathological conditions, but the attention devoted to their histology under non-pathological circumstances has been mostly academic or else rather perfunctory. Either the "ideal" textbook picture with its various well-defined layers was assumed to be normal or the theory that normal meninges vary in the thickness was accepted with very little concern for its implications.

With this situation in mind an attempt was made to learn something more about the average, non-neuropathological spinal cord so that the information could be used, as stated above, as a control for other spinal cord investigations. While some of the changes that occur are certainly due, as has been said, to the effect of general systemic disease on the nervous system, the more constant alterations due to advancing age are what chiefly command attention. Just when do these lesions first begin to appear? And is there any tendency toward a regular progression in their severity as age increases?

The pathology of the cord in old age is fairly well known, although most of the information was arrived at piecemeal. Disease of the blood vessels of the cord was reported by Webber[9] in 1882 and later by Campbell.[10] Thickening of the dura was first pointed out in 1855 by Rokitansky,[11] who observed even then that calcification occurs less often in the dura than in the pia-arachnoid. Charcot[12] first called at-

4

tention to the lipoid disease of the nerve cells that Nissl later called "pigmentary atrophy," and it is to Virchow that we are indebted for the knowledge that old nerve tissue is overrun with neuroglia.

Studies on the spinal cord that are confined to the effects of old age are not numerous but they are quite good. Campbell[10] in 1894 and Hamilton[13] again in 1910 (both using cords of mental patients, although ruling out as far as possible neurological disease) made thorough studies of senile changes. They both found arteriosclerosis, loss of myelin in lateral and posterior columns, hypertrophy of ependyma, and the presence of corpora amylacea. In addition Hamilton found the same fatty degeneration of nerve cells previously reported by Charcot and an overgrowth of glia in the degenerated tracts. In reviewing the whole subject in 1931 Critchley[14] was able to find very little additional in the literature.

This present study was attempted not so much in the hope of adding supplementary findings, as to ascertain when these degenerations first occur and to trace them through their ultimate development. No attempt, or at least very little, was made to correlate the histological findings with the systemic diseases of the patients, for there were too few cases of any one diagnosis in this series to make such a correlation valuable. Nevertheless any histological changes that were encountered, even though they had no connection with the process of aging, were mentioned and described, for the purpose of the study was to call attention to all alterations as they occur in the normal cord, regardless of their cause.

Thirty-one spinal cords were used in this series, ranging from the second through the ninth decade. The diseases were those commonly found in a general hospital—malignant hypertension, rheumatic heart disease, cancer of the stomach, miliary tuberculosis, etc.

The cords were studied in the following way. After a gross inspection blocks were cut from the cervical, thoracic, and lumbar levels and fixed in the appropriate solutions for frozen sections, celloidin, or paraffin embedding. Paraffin embedding was used only for Bodian preparations. Studies were made by using the following stains: hematoxylin and eosin, cresyl violet, van Gieson, Weigert (myelin), Weigert (elastic tissue), Bodian (axons), Oil red O (fat), and Holzer. In many cases to elucidate special points of interest, phosphotungstic acid hematoxylin, Hortega's silver carbonate, Dockrill's silver carbonate, and Cajal's gold sublimate were also used.

Second and Third Decades

This group comprises five cords from patients ranging in age from eleven through twenty-nine years. In each case the dura consists of even and regular collagenous bands with no patches of fibrous thickening and no evidence of calcification. The pia-arachnoid is more than filamentous, and in the van Gieson stain it appears as a substantial collagenous membrane measuring about 65 micra thick. It is somewhat thicker and denser over the anterior spinal artery. In one case there is a slight thickening over the dorsal aspect and a mild infiltration of lymphocytes and plasma cells on the ventral surface (Fig. 1). This cellular reaction is slight and consists of only twenty or thirty cells within the entire circumference of the section. Many of the cells are scattered in the region of the anterior spinal artery, but there is no perivascular cuffing. In another case the soft meninges are definitely thickened and measure about 85 micra. Over the dorsal surface of the cord they fit snugly up around the entering posterior roots (Fig. 2), and beyond the pial line an overgrowth of collagenous fibers extends centrally up into the substance of the cord toward the posterior horn. These fibers also extend peripherally into the posterior root, making a heavy endoneurium.

In the four youngest cases the white matter is solid and compact but in the twenty-nine-year-old case it is loose and slightly edematous, especially around the edge. In all cases the perivascular spaces are moderately dilated in the gray as well as in the white matter. In two cases there is a mild perivascular (adventitial) infiltration of lymphocytes, with occasional polymorphonuclear leucocytes or plasma cells scattered thinly throughout the gray and white matter at all levels of the cord. In four cases the central canal is patent and is bounded by a compact layer of ependymal cells. In the twenty-nine-year-old case, however, the cells of the central canal have begun to proliferate and are not only several rows deep but are also grouped in clusters near the canal in the gray commissure.

At all levels of the cords of the four youngest cases myelin sheath preparations show a slight paling around or close to the edges of the lateral and posterior columns. When seen in longitudinal section, the sheaths in these pale areas appear swollen. The bizarre myelin figures include granular and fragmented balls. In addition to this peripheral paling, the lupus erythematosus case shows a patch of demyelination close to the lateral pyramidal tract on one side. Compared with the anterior column, the posterior column is slightly and unevenly pale and the

6

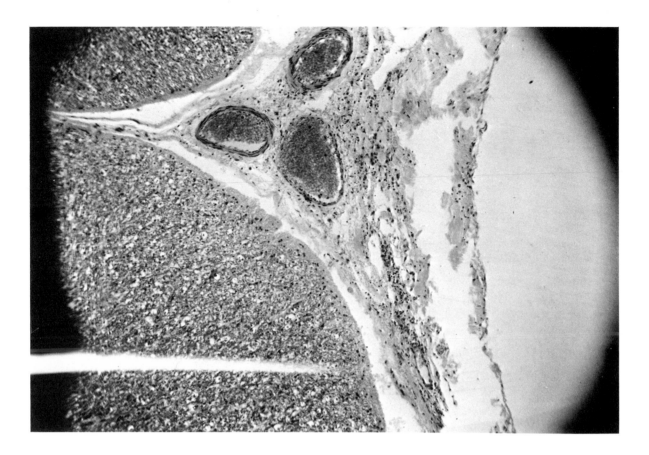

sheaths are more widely separated, giving the impression of slight degeneration, but on high power the individual sheaths show practically no swellings or fragments—they are merely farther apart. In one case, with collagenous overgrowth in the posterior roots, the paling and thinning are much more conspicuous, especially at the base of Goll's column near the posterior commissure; and some swelling of the sheaths and occasional myelin balls are visible on high power in longitudinal section. In all cases the posterior roots are practically normal, showing the conventional honeycombing or herringbone structure.

The silver stain for axons and neurofibrils shows that most of the axons are of uniform caliber and are distributed evenly at all levels of four cords. In the fifth cord no empty sheath spaces are seen on cross section, but the axons are packed a little more closely together in the posterior column, and on longitudinal section a few examples of fragmentation, beading, excessive tortuosity, and thickening of the axons are seen at all levels. The nerve roots show no changes. A few tan bodies, hyaline in character and having slightly crenated edges, are scattered in the anterior valley of the gray matter between the anteromedial and anterolateral cell groups at the cervical and lumbar levels of the fifth cord and at the cervical level of one other cord. These tan bodies occasionally have little wisps of neurofibril still attached to them like tails, and in some of the cords to be described later they are plainly seen in

Figure 1
Mild infiltration
of meninges.
H & E stain

7

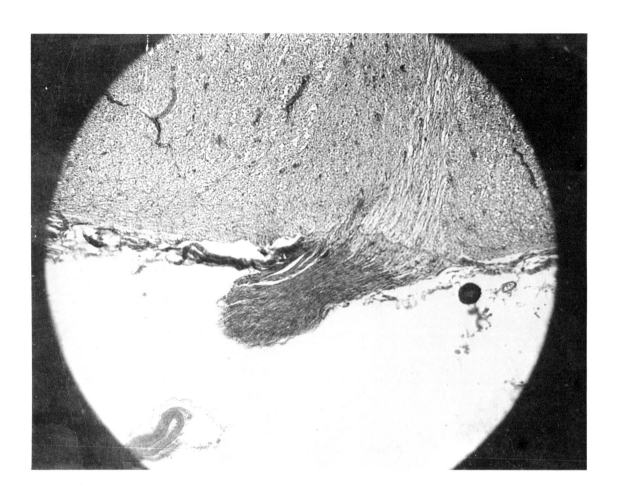

relation to the exiting nerve fibers of the anterior horn as they pass through the white matter of the cord. They are thus identified as swollen, chunky fragments of the neurofibrils of the anterior roots.

The motor cells of the anterior horn exhibit normal characteristics (Fig. 3) in four out of five cases. The cell bodies are moderately concave and the processes are visible for only a very short distance. The nuclei are centrally located, rounded, and clear and have dark nucleoli. The tigroid substance is in discrete masses, regularly shaped and arranged in rough rows in the manner customary for stichochrome cells. There is no lipofuchsin in most of the cells, but in the lupus case as well as in the twenty-nine-year-old case the lipochrome is occasionally very pale yellow and sometimes represents as much as 20 per cent of the cell volume. In the lupus case some of the cells of the thoracic region exhibit dense, heavy nuclear membranes and there is a certain amount of clumping of the Nissl substance. In the cervical and lumbar regions, as well, quite a few cells show a mild degree of central chromatolysis.

The cells of the lateral horn (Fig. 4) are somewhat different in each of the five cases. They vary in shape from fusiform to tortuous or even rounded. The nuclei are sometimes centrally placed, especially in the fusiform cells, and sometimes they are on the edge. In one case the

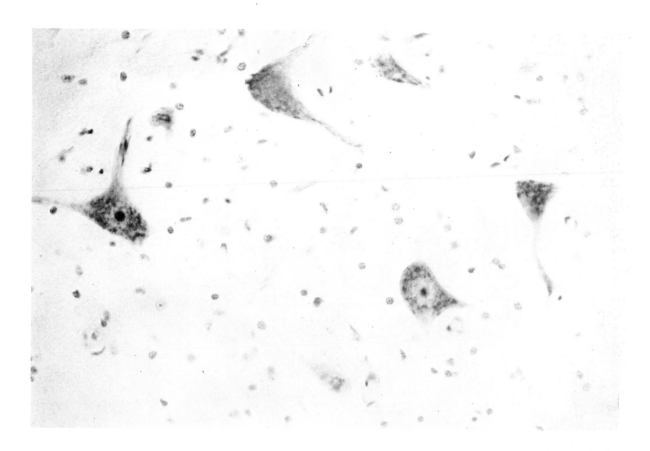

Figure 3
Normal anterior horn
cells at 16 years.
No lipochrome.
Nissl stain

nuclear membranes have many folds; in another (where the cell bodies are round) the nuclei are large and evidently swollen, for they occupy much of the cell volume, and the nucleoli are sometimes fragmented. The Nissl substance exhibits a regular and even stichochrome distribution in only one case. In another case there is some pyknosis and clumping of the tigroid bodies and in the remaining cases there are various degrees of chromatolysis—ranging from a pale, pulverized background studded with normal Nissl granules to a complete, generalized chromatolysis. No lipochrome is seen except in the twenty-nine-year-old case, where a slight amount of pale yellow pigment is visible.

Except in one case where there is distortion due to lipochrome, the cells in Clarke's column vary in form from rounded to lemon-shaped. The processes are scarcely visible in the Nissl stain, and when they are visible they can be seen only a very short distance. The nuclei are round, central and clear. In two cases the tigroid substance is present in large masses of about equal size, arranged concentrically after the manner of gyrochrome cells. In the other three cases there is central chromatolysis with discrete Nissl granules only around the edge. In four cases no lipochrome is present but in the twenty-nine-year-old case the lipochrome occupies as much as 75 per cent of the cell volume.

The glia, as seen chiefly in the Nissl and Holzer stains, already show many minor alterations in the second and third decades. The number

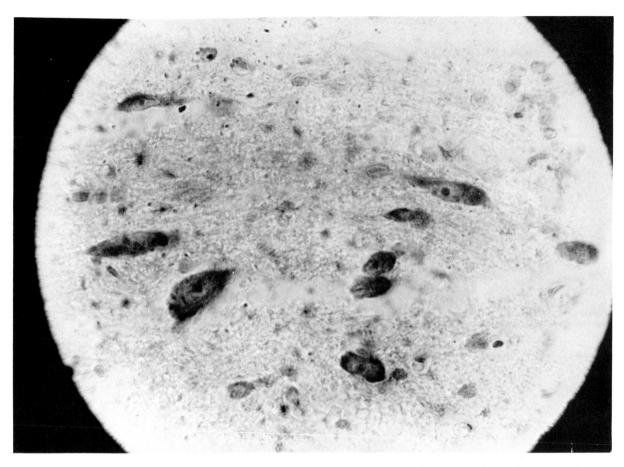

Figure 4
Normal lateral
horn cells.
Nissl stain

and distribution of glia cells are unaltered and regular only in the eleven-year-old case. Even here, in the white matter at all three levels, there are many astrocytes that are conspicuous because of pyknotic nuclei. In all the other cases there is an increase of astrocytes and oligodendroglia in the gray matter, the white matter, or both. This increase usually takes the form of a generalized or extensive, but very mild, hyperplasia. It is most conspicuous in Goll's column at the cervical and lumbar levels of the cord of the twenty-nine-year-old man and in both white and gray matter at all levels in the cord of the eleven-year-old boy (who died of rheumatic heart disease). In addition to these generalized reactions, in which the cytoplasm is usually hyperchromatic, there are indications of patchy reactions involving small groups of cells. Clusters of overstained astrocytes are scattered everywhere in the white matter of the lupus case, being often seen around blood vessels as glia stars and along the edge of the section near the pia. Sometimes the perivascular astrocytes are associated with lymphocytes or macrophages. The macroglia reaction in this case is a rather severe lesion. Besides occasional clusters of astrocytes in the white matter, the cord of the twenty-nine-year-old man shows hyperplastic microglia. These cells, in spite of their hyperchromatosis and their fairly conspicious proliferation, show only a slight degree of activation. Most of them re-

10

main about normal in size and show few if any swellings. They are often arranged in little clusters with which an astrocyte or two is occasionally associated. In the gray matter there are normally no satellites around the anterior horn cells, the lateral horn cells, or Clarke's column cells. As a consequence, glial reactions around diseased nerve cells is not a common finding. There are, however, rare instances of satellitosis around anterior horn cells in the one case that showed no generalized increase or change in the number or distribution of its glia. In four cases the gray matter also shows a few glial nodules in the anterior horns. Normally, Stilling's nucleus and the posterior horn cells often have satellites and no increase or diminution is observed in these cases. The Holzer picture corresponds, in general, to the cell findings. In the rheumatic heart disease case there is a proliferation of glial fibrils, mild but distinct, around the periphery of the gray matter bordering the anterior, lateral, and posterior columns. In another case there is a fairly strong posterior column gliosis in the lumbar region but none higher up. In another case there is a slight increase in glial fibrils around the pial edge of the white matter, and in the case with posterior column loss of myelin there is a faint posterior column gliosis.

The fat stain shows only one case that is entirely free from color in the anterior horn cells. The other cases, without exception, show only the faintest pink tinge, which in volume sometimes measures as much as 60 per cent of the cell. In the twenty-nine-year-old case the anterior horn cells are bright red, with fat measuring close to 90 per cent of the cell volume in some instances. This case also shows occasional perivascular fat-laden gitter cells in the posterior columns, as well as in the gray matter, and a slight fatty degeneration of the myelin in the lateral columns and in the entering posterior roots. No true myelin breakdown is seen anywhere. No corpora amylacea are seen in any of these cases.

The blood vessels in the meninges as well as those within the cord show no abnormalities.

11

Fourth Decade

There are three cases in this group. In each the dura is even, regular, and moderately thick, and shows no infiltration or calcification. The pia-arachnoid is likewise free from collagenous overgrowth and infiltrating cells. The white matter is slightly edematous and porous around the edge in all cases. The perivascular spaces are moderately dilated, especially in the gray matter, and in one case (coronary occlusion) the pericellular spaces are also unusually wide. There is no hematogenous reaction in two cases, but in the third a slight perivascular infiltration of lymphocytes is present in the gray matter in both the anterior and the posterior horns and a few of these cells are seen within the blood vessel walls. The central canal is slightly dilated in one case, and the ependymal cells are proliferating in the neighborhood of the central canal in all cases.

The Weigert stain shows a slight thinning and paling around the edge in one case, such as was seen in the youngest case of the first group. The posterior columns show a mild, diffuse thinning in all three cases. It is especially clear in Goll's column in two of these. This posterior column thinning is more marked than it was in any of the cases of the preceding group, except the twenty-nine-year-old case, which showed more degeneration than is usually found even late in the third decade. In addition, there is a small, but easily detected lesion in the pyramidal tract, evidently of the same age. This lesion, like those in the posterior columns, runs through the entire length of the cord. The posterior roots show no alterations.

The Bodian silver stain shows a few swollen axons in the anterior and lateral columns at the cervical and thoracic levels in one case as well as mild thickening of the posterior columns in all cases. In one case the widely separated fibers on one side of the pyramidal tract vary in thickness and are interspersed with glial nuclei. On longitudinal section slight moniliform swellings, thickenings, and excessive tortuosity are seen not only in the diseased pyramidal tracts but also in the posterior columns, where more destruction is apparent than the cross sections indicate. In one case (ulcerative colitis) there are a few tan bodies from diseased axons, between the anteromedial and anterolateral cell groups on one side at the cervical level. The opposite side shows no such lesion.

The nerve cells of the anterior horns present very few changes. In two cases practically nothing abnormal is found. The cells may be slightly shrunken in one case, but the nuclei are round and centrally

located; the Nissl granules are arranged in rows and there is very little lipochrome. In the third case some of the cells have pyknotic nuclei and the cell bodies are swollen and somewhat distorted. At all levels many cells show changes in the Nissl substance; some exhibit peripheral pyknosis with central chromatolysis and others show a pale, pulverized general chromatolysis. The majority of the cells have from one-eighth to one-half their volume occupied by lipochrome (Fig. 5). Throughout the cervical region many of the large cells of the lateral nuclei on both the right and the left side have a conspicuous incrustation of the Golgi net (Fig. 6).

Figure 5
Anterior horn cells:
lipochrome at 38 years.
Nissl stain

The lateral horn cells are rounded and look as if they may be swollen. The nuclei are round and voluminous and occupy a large part of the cell space. The Nissl granules are heavy and coarse around the edge and fine in the center and they are arranged sometimes concentrically and sometimes crescentically. There is no lipochrome.

The cells of Clarke's column are rounded or lemon-shaped and the nuclei are usually round, central, and clear. The Nissl substance is coarse and heavy all over the cell, or at least around the edge. In one case a few of the cells show large nuclear masses. Lipochrome is often present and occupies as much as 75 per cent of the cell volume.

There are very few changes in the glia in this decade. In two cases the number, distribution, and activity are all within normal limits. In

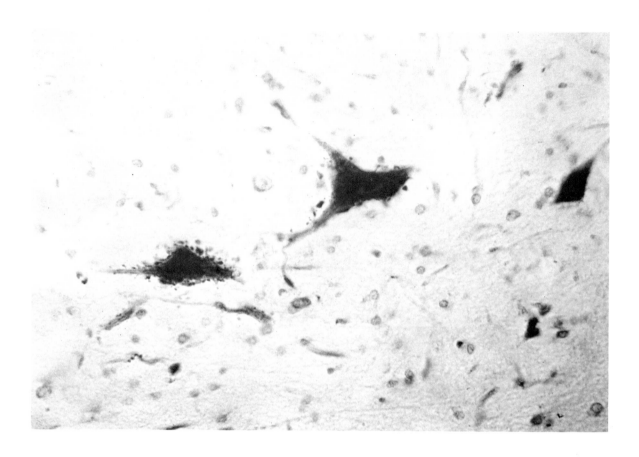

the third case there may be a slight generalized increase throughout the gray and white matter. In the pyramidal tract of this case there is an increased activation of astrocytes with hyperchromatosis and the production of "daughter cells," especially at the cervical and thoracic levels. In the gray matter of this case there are also a few instances of neuronophagia as well as a few glial nodules, which are composed of oligodendroglia and a few added microglia. The Holzer reaction is very slight everywhere, and the pyramidal tract lesion is seen only in the phosphotungstic acid stain.

The Oil red O stain for fat shows the pigment of the anterior horn cells to be a dull, rusty red occupying from 10 to 40 per cent of the cell volume. No bright red is present in these cells. The lateral column cells, in all instances, are only pale pink. In Clarke's column the pigment is in one mass, usually with occasional isolated granules. The cells are partly fatty, sometimes nearly 90 per cent of the cell being permeated by lipofuchsin. A few perivascular, fat-laden gitter cells are seen in various parts of the cord, especially near the diseased pyramidal tract, and also some fine gitter cells among the myelin sheaths. No actual fatty degeneration of the myelin sheath is seen. There is some fat in the endothelium of the blood vessels in one case but, aside from the mild lymphocytic infiltration of the vessel walls in the other cases mentioned above, there are no further vascular abnormalities.

Fifth Decade

There are six cases in this group, and in all of them the dura is of normal thickness, without any sign of calcification or inflammation. The leptomeninges are not hyperemic or really inflamed in any case, but in three cases there are signs of early thickening. In one case there is a thickening all around the cord throughout its entire length, while in two other cases the thickening is limited to the cervical and thoracic or the cervical and lumbar levels. In one of these a few scattered lymphocytes occur throughout the subarachnoid space and is most conspicious at the thoracic level where the meninges are slightly thickened. The other three cases show no thickening or infiltrations at all. In nearly all cases the white matter is loose or porous, especially around the edge. In one case the holes are large and filled with a slightly staining, metachromatic, colloidal substance. This edema of the substance of the cord is not altogether reflected in the perivascular and pericellular spaces. Where the holes are largest and the tissue most meshlike there sometimes is no perivascular distension at all. It is never marked, but in one instance, in the hematoxylin and eosin stain, the perivascular spaces contain a certain amount of bizarre-shaped vacuolated bodies.

Infiltrating lymphocytes and plasma cells, with an occasional polymorphonuclear, are to be seen around the blood vessels within the cord substance every now and then in four cases. In the other two cases they are not present. These collections of cells are most often found in the gray matter, and while they cannot be called definitely inflammatory, they represent a mild hematogenous reaction and are conspicuous enough to stand out in contrast to the rest of the tissue.

In this group of the fifth decade corpora amylacea are, for the first time, fairly numerous. They are present in five cases, although they are scanty and scattered. They are most numerous around the edge and in the posterior columns but can be found in any part of the white matter.

The central canal is patent, as in some of the earlier cases, and pyramidal cells not only line the canal but are also distributed in small groups or clusters in the neighboring region.

The nerve cells of the anterior horns show plenty of abnormalities. In only one case are the cells entirely free from alterations. The cell bodies are distinctly shrunken in two cases. One of these cases has cells of the chronic shrinkage type, with darkly staining cytoplasm; the nuclei are often pyknotic and the nuclear membranes show occasional folds.

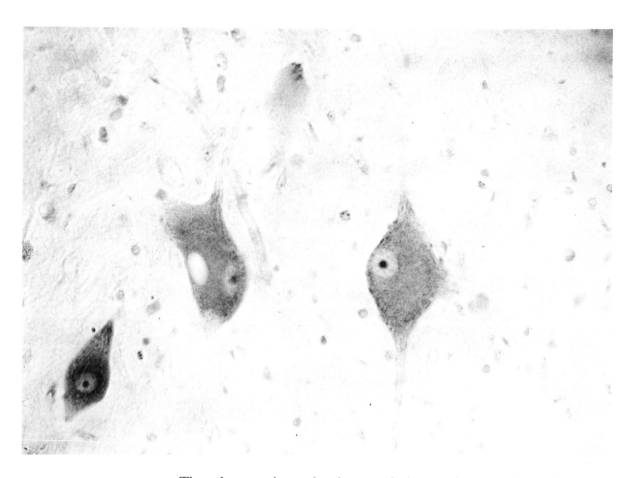

Figure 7
Anterior horn cells:
axonal reaction
with vacuoles.
Nissl stain

The other case has pale, chromatolytic cytoplasm and hyperchromatic processes that extend for considerable distance. The latter are quite tortuous. The nuclei are not conspicious except for very dark nucleoli. These typically ischemic cells are present at all levels. Another case has a few swollen cells at all levels. These cells are not vacuolated and do not look severely diseased, but they occur in the neighborhood of cells that have evidently disappeared abiotrophically for empty cell spaces remain without glial activity. In another case, the anterior horn cells show pronounced axonal reaction (Fig. 7), especially at the cervical and lumbar levels, with generalized chromatolysis of the Nissl substance. These cells have pale, eccentric nuclei and are greatly swollen. Some of them have vacuoles. The lipofuchsin varies in amount in different cases from none to 75 per cent. It is usually concentrated in one mass and centrally located, although in the big cells showing axonal reaction it is often pushed to one pole. In the more normal-looking cells the discrete tigroid granules can be seen overlying the lipochrome.

The lateral horn cells are swollen, or at least rounded, in every case. The majority are irregular in outline but have thick, rounded centers. The nuclei are eccentric and are sometimes round and sometimes leaf-shaped; the nuclear membranes are frequently folded. Two cases show cells with hyperchromatic Nissl substance around the edge and central

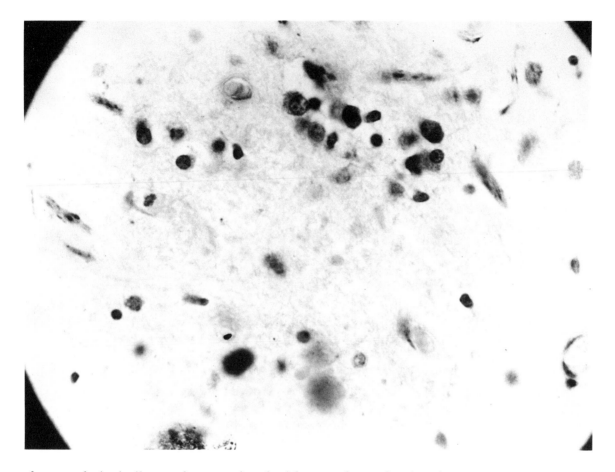

chromatolysis similar to that associated with axonal reaction in other types of cells. In two cases the swollen cell bodies contain vacuoles. There is very little lipochrome in any of these cells, and when present it is usually located close to the nucleus.

Figure 8
Anterior horn:
glial nodules.
Nissl stain

The cells of Clarke's column have few unusual features. The cell bodies and nuclei are conventional, but the Nissl substance is sometimes chromatolytic not only in the center, but also in the periphery. The lipofuchsin is abundant, sometimes occupying as much as 95 per cent of the cell volume, and often serves as a background for the large, discrete Nissl bodies.

No case shows a generalized increase of microglia, but in one case there is a widespread increase of oligodendroglia and astrocytes in the anterior horn, and in another there is a noticeable hyperplasia of astrocytes in the posterior column and around the edges of the posterior and lateral columns. Occasional glial nodules of oligodendrocytes appear in the anterior horns (Fig. 8) of three cases, and examples of perivascular gliosis are found in the white matter of the malignant hypertension case.

The Holzer stain shows no reaction in three cases. In the other three the posterior columns are seen to have a mild gliosis, and on longitudinal section its isomorphic character is visible. A mild gliosis appears around the periphery of the posterior and lateral columns (es-

17

pecially at the cervical level) in one case and at the boundary of the gray and white matter around the anterior horns in two cases.

In the Weigert stain the posterior roots show no change in two cases and very little change, until after the root passes through the pia, in two others. In the remaining cases the lesions are fairly conspicuous; myelin swelling, ball formation, and paling are distinctly seen. Many myelin figures are present inside the cord, where the posterior root joins the posterior horn.

There are various degrees of thinning and paling around the edge of the cord itself in four cases; in one of them the peripheral thinning is similar to but milder than the honeycomb type seen in pernicious anemia. The lateral columns of two cases show some thinning and paling —in one case to a mild degree and in the other to a degree severe enough to suggest a cerebral accident. The posterior columns of all six cases show various degrees of degeneration, sometimes evenly scattered through the whole funiculus and sometimes more conspicuous in Goll's column. These lesions are seen to best advantage in the cervical sections. The malignant hypertension case shows some perivascular demyelination in all columns of the white matter, and as a consequence it looks older than the others in this group. On high power and on longitudinal section there is corroboration of the above-mentioned myelin lesions. Swelling, ballooning, paling, and the formation of myelin balls and other myelin figures, especially around the edge and in the posterior columns, are common findings.

Silver impregnation shows a condensation of axons in the posterior columns, and especially in Goll's column, on cross section in four cases; the axons are closer together and the intervening sheaths are thinner than in the other columns. There are a few empty sheath spaces in the lateral as well as the posterior columns. In one case there are not many empty sheaths, but the axons are often thicker and in the anterior valley between the anteromedial and anterolateral nuclei a few tan bodies are present. In four cases there is a considerable variation in the character of axons in the posterior columns; some of them are very thin and others very thick. On longitudinal section it is seen that the thin axons have parallel sides and the thick axons show great variations in caliber, resulting in beading, ballooning, vacuolization, fragmentation, and tortuosity. In the malignant hypertension case the axons that pass through the multiple small foci of softening are destroyed in the conventional manner.

The fat stain shows lipoid in various amounts from none to 90 per cent of the anterior horn cell volume in different cases. The color likewise varies from orange-pink to bright red. The red pigment sometimes appears in small droplets but more often in large masses, either round or concentric in shape. The cells with axonal reaction mostly show bright red, concentrically arranged lipoid. The cells of the lateral columns have a rusty red lipoidal content, usually no higher than 10 per cent of the estimated cell volume. The cells of Clarke's column also have a

18

dull red lipoidal content, which sometimes measures as much as 80 per cent. Perivascular, fat-laden gitter cells are scattered through all columns of the cords at all levels. Not so many perivascular gitters are seen in the gray matter, and relatively few fat-bearing corpuscles are seen outside the perivascular spaces free in the nerve tissue. There are occasional scattered droplets of fat in the posterior columns in three cases, especially at the cervical level, and there are some swollen, fatty sheaths, especially in the foci of softening, in the malignant hypertension case. In two other cases fatty droplets can be found in the blood vessel walls, and in one of them fatty degeneration is present in practically every vessel. Aside from the fat in the walls of these vessels, both cases show a proliferation and thickening of the intima with considerable reduction in the size of the lumina of some of the meningeal vessels, most particularly the anterior spinal artery as seen in the van Gieson stain.

Sixth Decade

There are seven cases in this group, and every one of them shows a slight thickening of the pia-arachnoid even though the dura cannot really be said to show much alteration. There is no infiltration in two cases, but the other three show a scattering of lymphocytes and plasma cells that are most conspicuous in the region of the anterior spinal artery at the various levels of the cord.

The white matter is porous and edematous in all cases but one. Fenestrations occur, especially around the edge and posteriorly. The perivascular spaces are sometimes dilated in cases that show edema. In the case that shows no edema of the nervous tissue the perivascular spaces are widely dilated and the adventitia is markedly edematous. Only one case shows perivascular infiltration (aside from that in the meninges); in the exceptional case there are small perivascular collections of lymphocytes and plasma cells in the gray matter at the thoracic and lumbar levels.

Corpora amylacea appear around the edge of every cord in this group but are not very numerous except in two cases. In the lymphoblastoma and uremia cases they are very conspicuous and are widely distributed over the entire section at all levels.

The central canal shows a moderate amount of proliferation of its ependymal cells around a slightly patent lumen in four cases. Another case shows an exaggeration of this condition with a widely dilated canal at some levels and a reduplication of the central canal at other levels; the customary clusters of ependymal cells are also scattered throughout the gray commissure in this region. Many subependymal glia can be seen even in the hematoxylin and eosin stain.

The nerve cells of the anterior horn continue to show alterations. In one case they exhibit chronic shrinkage, with pyknotic and hyperchromatic cytoplasm, staining a long way out on the processes; a pyknotic nucleus; and an estimated 30 per cent of the cell volume taken up by lipochrome. In two other cases the total volume of the cells is increased and the cell bodies are distorted by lipochrome, which sometimes occupies as much as 90 per cent of any one cell. Under such circumstances the nucleus is pushed to one side and various bulges, one of which may contain the nucleus, appear on the cell. The remaining Nissl substance is squeezed aside, most of it forming a dark peripheral ring and a large mass of lipochrome occupies most of the cell space. Sometimes a few discrete, pyknotic masses of Nissl substance can be

20

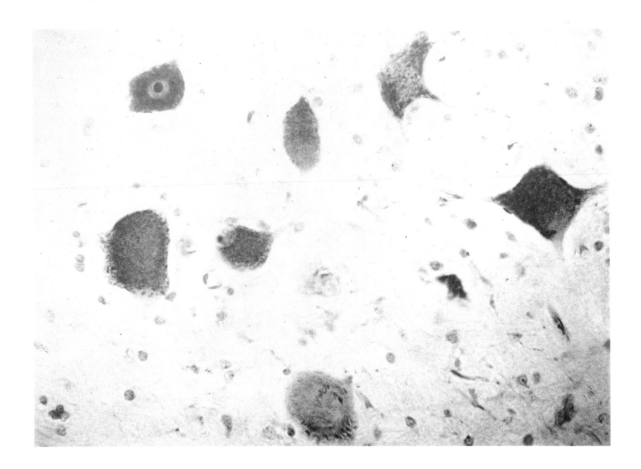

seen overlying the lipofuchsin. In one of these cases the most swollen
and distorted cells show a few fair-sized vacuoles. In two other cases
there is early axonal reaction; the cell bodies are swollen, the nuclei eccentric, the cytoplasm chromatolytic (Fig. 9). The lipochrome, while
scanty in one case, is conspicuous in the other (uremia). In the latter
some of the cell bodies are actually fractured and lipochrome occupies
most, or all, of one of the fragments.

Figure 9
Anterior horn cells:
early axonal reaction.
Nissl stain

None of the lateral horn cells are free from changes (Fig. 10). In
every case the cell bodies are swollen, or at least rounded and plump,
and in only one case do any of them retain the fusiform shape and character seen in the early decades. The round nuclei are usually close to
the edge and folds are frequently present in the nuclear membranes.
The Nissl substance is seen most regularly around the periphery and the
central part of many cells is chromatolytic. The lipochrome is not very
abundant in these cases, in one of which only the larger cells show any.
In the other two cases there is a copious lipofuchsin deposit, resulting in
bulging, distorted cells in one case, and vacuolated cells in the other.

The cells of Clarke's column are round and regular in four cases and
distorted by bulges in only one. The nuclei are centrally located unless
pushed to one side by pigment and they are round and clear. There is
a central chromatolysis in three cases, with the remaining tigroid bodies

21

arranged near the cell margin. In one case there are a few cells with small vacuoles. The lipochrome is characteristically abundant in all cases except one but in this one it is scarcely discernible.

The Weigert picture shows more definite evidence of disease in this decade. The posterior roots exhibit swelling, ballooning, fragmentation of the myelin to a more or less mild degree, and some free myelin balls. Myelin figures are seen frequently inside the pia, as the posterior root joins the posterior horn. In all but one of the cords of this decade the posterior columns are thinner and paler than in the cords of the fourth decade. At the cervical, thoracic, and lumbar levels the exceptional cord resembles that of a person in the eighth decade—the sheaths are swollen and widely separated and the tracts are pale, especially near the raphe. Small linear patches of thinning appear in the lateral columns and along the edge of the cord at all levels. The posterior column thinning is usually more accentuated in Goll's column and it runs consistently through all levels. But in one case there is a unilateral thinning and paling in Goll's column at the lumbar level that is not seen higher up. All cases show peripheral paling, mostly in the lateral region. In one case an old pyramidal tract lesion appears unilaterally at the cervical level but not at the thoracic and lumbar levels. In another case there is a distinct perivascular demyelination in the lateral and posterior columns, especially at the thoracic and lumbar levels, in the Weigert stain but the blood vessels are conspicuous in other stains. These perivascular lesions are in no instance extensive, but on high power they show the characteristic myelin figures that are so plainly visible in longitudinal sections of the more general lesions in the posterior and lateral columns.

The Bodian impregnation shows a picture that corroborates the Weigert findings. The axons of the posterior columns, especially Goll's, are swollen at all levels in all cases. Sometimes the fibers are more densely packed around the edge and in Goll's column. A fair number of empty sheath spaces appear not only in Goll's column but also in the lateral columns and around the edge. In one case minute foci of softening appear in the white matter and on longitudinal section the axons are seen to be fragmented as they pass through these spots. In the remaining cases, the affected zones show swelling, thickening, beading, tortuosity, and fragmentation. Tan bodies are present in only one case, and in this case not in the upper cord but only at the lumbar level between the anteromedial and anterolateral cell groups.

In most cases there is an increase in microglia around the edge of the cord and in the posterior columns. The only case in which there is very little increase in glial nuclei is the one that shows excessive myelin loss in the posterior columns. The Holzer picture shows not only a strong reaction but a rather dense gliosis, especially near the raphe. In the case with multiple central canals, clusters of astrocytes and oligodendroglia are conspicuous in the gray commissure. In every case there are spotty increases of astrocytes and oligodendroglia in the white matter.

22

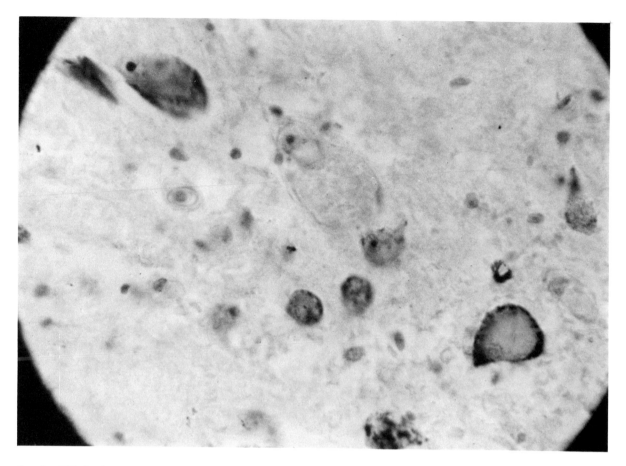

In the Nissl picture these small nests of cells show hyperstainable cytoplasm with distinct processes, dividing astrocytes, and clumps of oligodendroglia. Swollen oligodendroglia, especially in the white matter, are
a commonplace finding. Glial nodules are present in the anterior horns.
In one case the perivascular astrocytes are more numerous and more
stainable. This is the case with perivascular loss of myelin. In another
case the Nissl picture shows an increase in the number of nuclei and the
Holzer picture shows a strong gliosis at the junction of the gray and
white matter, especially around the anterior horns and most particularly
at the cervical level. The Holzer findings in the other cases are all
commensurate with the myelin loss.

Figure 10
Lateral horn cells:
swelling, hyalin-like
cytoplasm.
Nissl stain

The lipoid shows up as bright red in the anterior horn cells of all
but one case. Ordinarily the fat is in one mass, either rounded or cres-
cent-shaped. The amount varies in different cells in different cases, as
it does in different cells in the same case; some cells show none while
others show as much as 95 per cent of their volume to be occupied by
the fatty mass. Usually between 40 and 70 per cent can be found. In
the case with the greatest volume the dull brick-red of the anterior horn
cells contrasts with the brilliant red of the cells in Clarke's column. In
all except one case the cells in Clarke's column show a fairly bright red.
Here the rusty brown contrasts with the bright red of the anterior horn

23

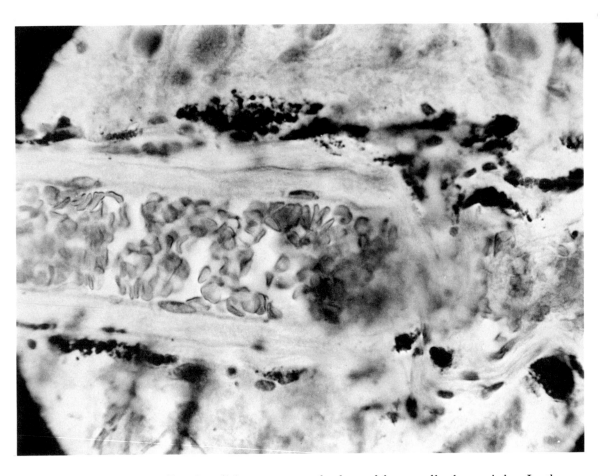

Figure 11
Perivascular gitter cells.
Oil red O stain

cells. In all but one case the lateral horn cells show pink. In the exceptional case they show what seems to be axonal reaction; here instances of bright red color indicate degeneration within the nucleus. In many cases a large number of small posterior horn cells show fat in various degrees. The ependymal cells of the central canal, as well as occasional glia in that neighborhood, exhibit granules of bright red fat. Fat-laden perivascular gitter cells (Fig. 11) are present fairly often in the gray matter and are distributed rather widely throughout the white matter, especially in the posterior and lateral columns. Free balls of fat are found occasionally in the posterior columns and along the periphery in most cases. In the case with the large amount of myelin loss fat droplets and swollen pinkish myelin sheaths are seen in the posterior roots within the cord. This fatty reaction is much milder than the Weigert preparations indicate. The myelin figures seen on longitudinal section are all pale pink.

In one case the endothelium of the blood vessel walls contains fat and the adventitia is thickened. The anterior spinal artery has a proliferation of the intima with a consequent diminution in the size of the lumina in two cases and a slight thickening of the media in one case. In one case the blood vessels seem very conspicuous, because of their increase in number, but inspection of individual vessels shows no signs of disease.

24

Seventh Decade

There are six cases in this group. The pia-arachnoid is thickened and the dura is moderately thickened in every case at all levels throughout the entire circumference of the cord (Fig. 12). In most instances these collagenous fibers stick close to the cord tissue, but in one instance a thick, loose envelope encircles an apparently shrunken cord. There is a mild infiltration of lymphocytes and plasma cells in three cases and in one of these the fibroblastic response is quite marked.

As in the preceding groups, the white matter is edematous and porous, especially around the edge, in all but one case, where the cord is presumably shrunken. The perivascular spaces are correspondingly dilated in all but two cases (one of them the shrunken cord). There is a slight perivascular infiltration of lymphocytes in two cases, in one of which an occasional polymorphonuclear is also present. This infiltration occurs in the gray matter and, although mild, can be found at all levels.

Corpora amylacea are present in all cases, although in two cases they are rather scarce. They are more plentiful in the dorsal half of the cord, especially in the posterior columns and around the edge. Sometimes they are found well out near the meninges. In one case they are especially conspicuous around the edge; they are found in the posterior roots as far out as the pial line, where they abruptly cease.

There is some proliferation of the cells lining the central canal in four cases. In the other two, a single layer of ependymal cells can be found in nearly all sections.

The anterior horn cells of five cases show the characteristic bulging and distortion, due to lipochrome, that is so often found in advanced age (Fig. 13). Eccentric nuclei are often seen in such cases, being pushed to one side by the pigment, and occasionally these nuclei are darkened and pyknotic. In one cord they are particularly pyknotic at the thoracic level; where the anteromedial cells are markedly shrunken. In addition to their decreased size and increased concavity of outline, these cells show relatively increased lipochrome. This is unusual, because the anteromedial cells of most cords are but scantily supplied with lipofuchsin. In contrast, the lateral column cells of this same cord show marked swelling, distortion, and pigmentary atrophy at the cervical and lumbar levels. In another cord in this group the cells show very little lipochrome and this is bluish green. Judged by the small amount of lipofuchsin, the cells seem too young for a sixty-five-year-old cord.

25

Figure 12
Thickening of the meninges
at 68 years.
Nissl stain

But it is then seen that the cells are pale and considerably shrunken and the processes are hyperchromatic. Generalized chromatolysis is widespread throughout the cord and only a few tigroid bodies are left. Chromatolysis is absent from only one cord of this age group. In this case the Nissl bodies appear in large masses throughout the cells. The chromatolysis in the four other cases is sometimes generalized and sometimes only central. When it is central, the remaining tigroid bodies are pyknotic and are arranged around the periphery as large discrete bodies. The lipochrome, except in the one case where it is scanty and bluish green, is golden yellow and abundant, sometimes occupying as much as 95 per cent of the cell volume and surrounded by only a delicate rim of cytoplasm. Occasionally a cell has entirely disappeared with only a mass of lipochrome remaining to mark its former site.

The lateral horn cells are elongated and fusiform in only one case. In all the rest they are swollen and rounded and in two instances contain vacuoles. As a rule, the nuclei are round and possibly swollen, but in one case they are shrunken and the membranes exhibit folds. In one cord the cell picture suggests an axonal reaction; the cell bodies are rounded and swollen, the nuclei are eccentric, and there is central chromatolysis with peripheral clumping. There is some degree of chromatolysis in every case. Sometimes it is generalized, sometimes only central, and in one case it is partly generalized, with the remaining

26

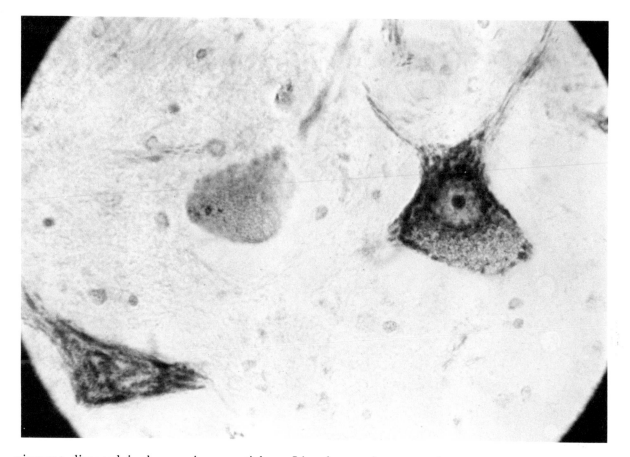

pigment disposed in long, wispy particles. Lipochrome is present in every case, occupying from 30 per cent to 70 per cent of the cell volume.

In three cases the cells of Clarke's column are practically without change, except for some slight chromatolysis. In two other cases there is swelling and distortion due to lipochrome, and in one of these cases the pigmentary atrophy is so marked that only a thin rim of cytoplasm (or none at all) remains to enclose the pigment. This is the same case in which the anterior horn cells show such extreme atrophy. Eccentric nuclei, central chromatolysis (Fig. 14), peripheral pyknosis, and dense masses of lipochrome (occupying 90 per cent of the cell volume) appear in the remaining case.

In five cases the Weigert preparations reveal thinning and paling around the edges at virtually all levels. The lesions are less consistent at the thoracic level than they are at the cervical and lumbar levels. In one case the thinning has a punched-out, porous appearance like that found in pernicious anemia. The lateral columns exhibit generalized thinning in five cases, two of which show perivascular demyelination on both sides. In all six cases the posterior columns are more or less degenerated in some parts of their course. In two cases, one with faint thinning near the commissure and the other with slightly generalized thinning, the degeneration is not so severe as would be expected for this decade. In the other cases the posterior column lesions are most notice-

Figure 13
Anterior horn cells:
lipochrome at 66 years.
H & E stain

27

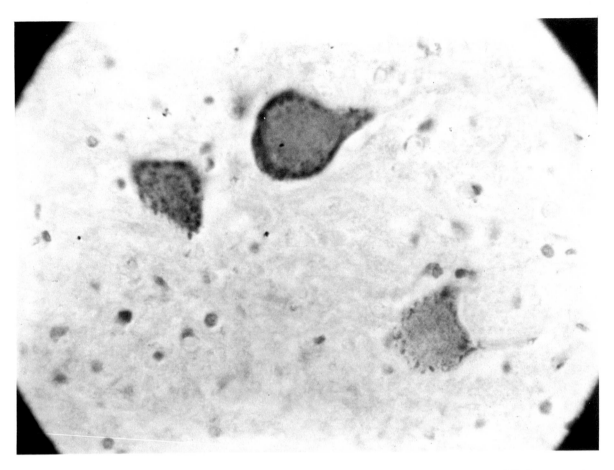

Figure 14
Clarke's column cells:
central chromatolysis.
Nissl stain

able near the tip of Goll's column or near the raphe. High power inspection of both cross and longitudinal sections shows swelling, ballooning, and myelin balls interrupting the courses of fibers. These lesions are conspicuous around the blood vessels of the two cases with lesions of the perivascular type. The posterior roots show swelling, ballooning, fragmentation, and myelin balls in only three cases, although myelin figures are more often found inside the pial line.

In the silver stain axons are seen to vary in thickness, number, and concentration in different cords as well as at different levels. Empty sheath spaces, with a consequent sparseness of axons, appear quite consistently in the posterior columns and frequently in lateral columns close to the periphery of the cord. The axons are sometimes irregular in shape and so swollen that in cross section they are four or five times larger than the thin ones. Swollen and notched axons also appear in the pyramidal tracts of two cords. On longitudinal section one finds swelling, thickening, beading, vacuolization, fragmentation, and tortuosity in all cases. Even the two cases with very slight myelin loss exhibit fairly severe axon lesions. Tan bodies (those greatly thickened, discrete fragments of axon, seen in the valley between the anteromedial and anterolateral cell groups) are present in three cases. In two cases they appear at both the cervical and the lumbar level, but in one case they are present only in

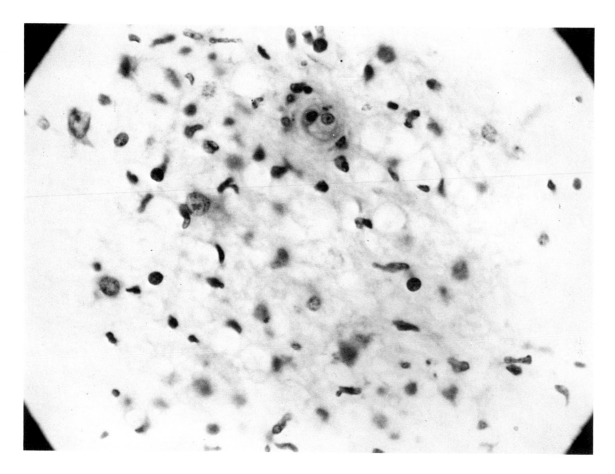

the lumbar region. The posterior root fibers are swollen and thickened in a few instances.

The glia picture is consistent with the previous findings. In general there is an increase in glial nuclei. Astrocytes are especially abundant around the edges of the cords and in the posterior columns and often in the lateral columns. This hyperplasia is found at all levels of the cords but is most conspicuous in the posterior and lateral columns at the cervical level. The peripheral increase is perhaps most marked in the lumbar region. In the gray matter of these cases there is some hyperplasia of astrocytes and oligodendroglia, the latter being usually found in minute nodules. In the white matter there are minute nests of astrocytes and microglia (Fig. 15), especially in the posterior and lateral columns. The astrocytes are usually overstained; the cytoplasm is extensive and daughter cell formation is quite common. The microglia, while numerous and hyperchromatic, show very little activity. Most of them are in the resting stage. Aside from the glial nodules in the anterior horn, there are no signs of neuronophagia but in one case the cells of Clarke's column exhibit a mild degree of satellitosis. As seen in the Holzer stain, gliosis is conspicuous in one case, especially at the lumbar level; there the whole white matter of all columns is densely gliosed. This is one of the cases in which there is a perivascular gliosis. In the

Figure 15
Focus of microglia
in white matter.
Nissl stain

29

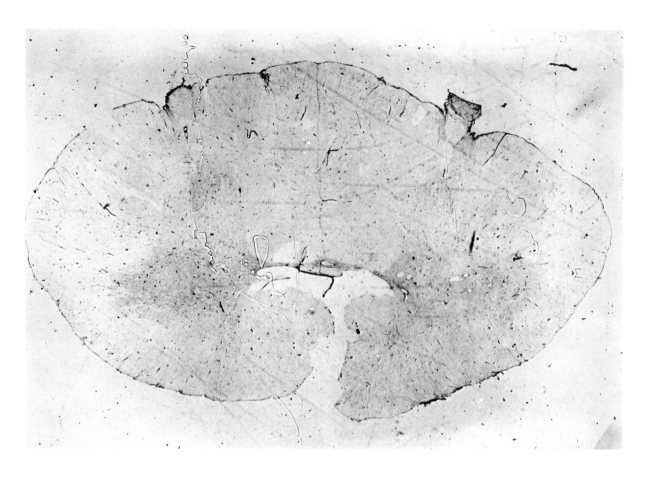

other cases most of the gliosis is found around the periphery of the cord, around the edge of the gray matter, and in the posterior and anterior horns (Figs. 16 A–C). On longitudinal section the gliosis is seen to be nearly entirely isomorphic.

The lipoid in the anterior horns is orange-red in one case and bright red in the others. It occupies between 75 and 95 per cent of the cell volume. The lipoid in Clarke's column is usually pinker and paler and in larger granules than that in the anterior horns, and it pushes the nuclei to one side. There are occasional fatty myelin sheaths scattered throughout the posterior columns; in one case a pyramidal tract shows what is evidently a fresh lesion. This was not conspicuous in the Weigert preparations. Fat-laden perivascular gitter cells are to be seen here and there with some frequency in the white matter, especially in the posterior columns. In two cases they are found in the gray matter, in the posterior horns. The central canal cells and many glia cells in their immediate vicinity contain fat.

The blood vessels of the meninges exhibit a moderate thickening of the media in one case and an intimal proliferation in two cases. In one case blood pigment is present in the intimal cells, and in the other the small artery on one side of the central canal is occluded by internal proliferation.

30

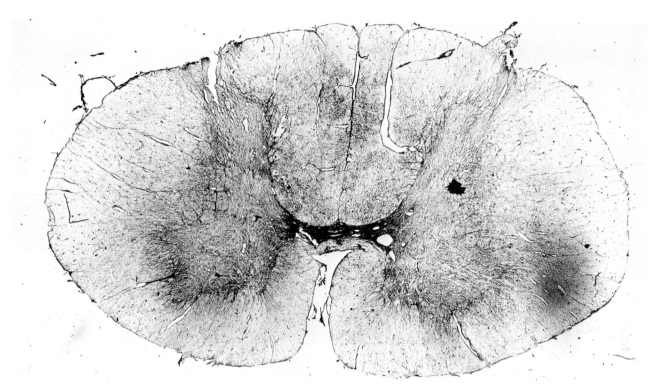

Figure 16B. Gliosis of anterior horn and slight gliosis of posterior column at 45 years. Holzer stain

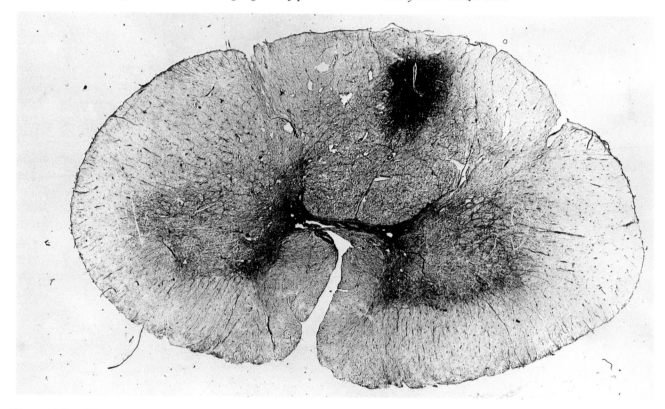

Figure 16C. Gliosis of anterior horn and posterior column at 82 years. Holzer stain

31

Eighth Decade

There are three cases in this group. The dura in all three cases is very thick (from 350 to 500 micra), but there is little increase over what is found in the seventh decade.

The pia-arachnoid is free from infiltration in two cases, and in one cord there is no thickening. In the other two cases, however, the collagenous strands are swollen and the pia-arachnoid is thickened all around the cord at all three levels. In one case, at the lumbar level, the leptomeninges fit closely around the entering posterior root, and connective tissue strands can be seen running longitudinally among the root fibers. In this case there are a few lymphocytes and plasma cells in the subarachnoid space, especially near the anterior spinal artery. The white matter has a dense consistency in two cases, while in the third it is porous and edematous. The perivascular spaces and pericellular spaces are moderately distorted in all cases. No inflammatory cells are present, except those mentioned in the meninges. The ependyma of the central canal has proliferated, and in one case it has closed the canal, which is surrounded by ependymal cells five or six layers deep. Corpora amylacea are present in all cases, but they are more abundant posteriorly.

The nerve cells of the anterior horn are either shrunken or swollen with lipochrome in all cases. The shrunken cells are invariably hyperchromatic. The exaggeratedly concave cell bodies are dark and the processes are long and tortuous. The nuclei also are pyknotic and darkened. Sometimes pyknotic Nissl granules are clumped around a nucleus. The rest of the pigment is dense and consolidated. The cells that do not show shrinkage exhibit various stages of pigmentary atrophy, especially in the lateral nuclei at the cervical and lumbar levels. The cell bodies show a good deal of distortion and bulging, depending upon the amount of lipofuchsin present. In some instances conspicuous vacuoles are found in the pigment. Sometimes only the pigment remains to mark the site of a former cell. In no case are these atrophic cells accompanied by neuronophagia.

The lateral horn cells do not have the consistently rounded shape so frequently met with in the later decades. In all three cases there are many fusiform, wavy, or tortuous cells, although swollen, leaf-shaped or rounded cells are sometimes present. The nuclei are eccentric and there are occasional folds in the nuclear membranes. The Nissl substance shows no chromatolysis but the granules are sometimes clumped and dark. In one case there is a certain amount of pigmentary atrophy,

32

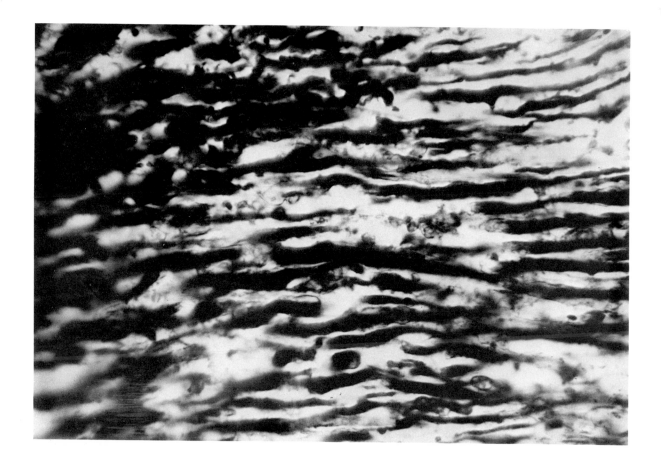

with the lipochrome occupying as much as 50 per cent of the cell volume and the remaining Nissl substance forming a mere framework for the pigment.   In the other cases the lipofuchsin is relatively scanty.

In all three cords the cells of Clarke's column are rounded or piriform, with the nuclei sometimes on the edge.   There is chromatolysis, either general or central, in all cases.   When the chromatolysis is central, the remaining Nissl substance is clumped peripherally.   The lipochrome is abundant in all these cells, often occupying more than an estimated 90 per cent of the cell volume.   In one case, at least, the cells look definitely atrophic.

The Weigert stain shows a pyramidal tract lesion in both the crossed and corresponding uncrossed pathways of one cord.   Aside from this lesion, which is obviously from a cerebral infarction, all three cords show mildly diffuse thinning in the lateral columns and around the edge. Also there is a slight perivascular demyelination in all columns at all levels of all cords.   The posterior columns exhibit the expected, customary advance in severity of demyelination.   It is especially noticeable in Goll's column near the raphe at the cervical level; lower down, particularly at the lumbar level, it is more diffuse.   The posterior roots show swelling and myelin balls (Fig. 17) in all cases and in one case there is considerable variation in the caliber of the incoming fibers; some are of

Figure 17
Posterior root:
Myelin figures and
alterations in sheath.
Weigert stain

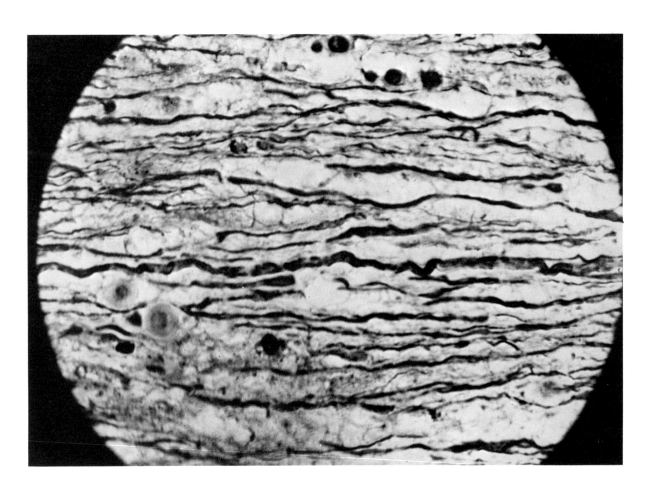

Figure 18
Longitudinal
section of cord:
alterations in axons.
Bodian stain

the usual diameter while many are very thin. As the thin fibers maintain their caliber throughout their course and are only slightly swollen, they are probably not abnormal but merely very conspicuous in this case. Aside from the pyramidal tract lesion (which must be discounted), the high power picture of the cord shows swollen sheaths and myelin figures, both perivascular and general in various parts of the white matter, especially the posterior columns. The sheaths of the posterior columns are not only swollen but, when seen on cross section, they are rather widely separated.

The axon impregnation shows the fibers of the diseased pyramidal tracts to be closer together and a condensation of the remaining fibers, with loss of sheath spaces. In the posterior columns and to a slighter extent in the lateral columns, as well as around the edge, there are many empty sheath spaces, with rather widely separated axons as a consequence. On cross section the axons often look swollen and notched or pear-shaped. On longitudinal section swelling, thickening, beading, granulation, tortuosity, and fragmentation appear in all cases but are especially marked in one (Fig. 18). Here the anterior horn is generously spotted with tan bodies (Fig. 19) throughout the lumbar region. In another case the nerve roots show marked thickening and swelling.

34

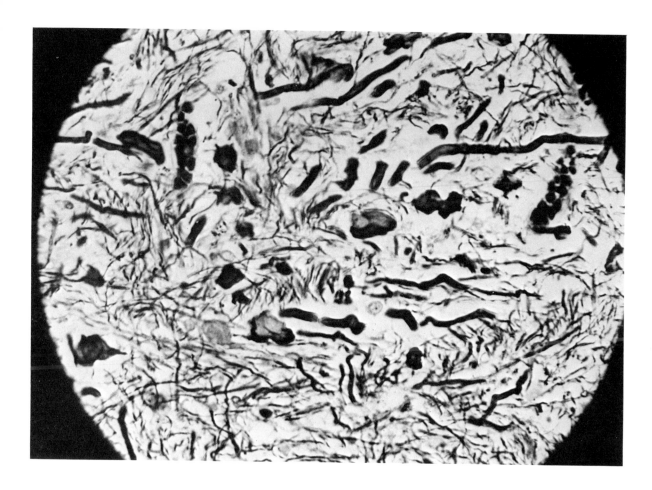

Glia are present in increased numbers in all cases; astrocytes and oligodendroglia are the most conspicuous in two cases but all three types are extremely conspicuous in the third case. These hyperchromatic cells are widely distributed throughout the gray and white matter. In one case a few nodules of oligodendroglia can be found in the gray matter at any level. In another case microglia can be seen in profusion, but mostly in the resting state, in the gray matter of all segments. The gray matter shows a generalized hyperplasia of astrocytes, especially near the border where the gray matter comes in contact with white matter, in all cases. In the white matter the astrocytes are greatly increased in size and number; the distribution is generalized and widespread, but a few are seen in little nests in association with a few microglia. This increase is especially noticeable in the posterior columns and around the periphery, where a dense ring of astrocytes lies. In one case, in addition, there is a strong perivascular gliosis, so conspicuous that the membrana gliosa limitans is beautifully seen in the Nissl stain. There is also a marked activation of astrocytes in the gray commissure near the central canal. Satellitosis, or something resembling it, with a few oligodendroglia or astrocytes in association with nerve cells, is seen in the anterior horns of two cases. The Holzer picture (Fig. 20) shows a corresponding in-

Figure 19
Tan bodies in valley
between anteromedial
and anterolateral
cell groups.
Bodian stain

35

crease in glial fibrils. In all cases these are distributed in moderate profusion throughout the gray matter and are especially prominent in the area where the gray matter comes in contact with the white matter. Marked gliosis appears in the posterior columns, particularly that of Goll. In one case there is a strong gliosis at the junction of Burdach's column with the gray matter of the commissure and the posterior horn. In two cases the pyramidal tracts are more gliosed on one side than on the other.

The fat in the anterior horn cells is bright red and frequently occupies as much as 80 per cent of the cell volume. The cells of Clarke's column and the lateral horn cells show less color and no fatty degeneration. There is no real fatty degeneration of the myelin, except for a small amount in the pyramidal tract of one case. Fat-laden perivascular gitter cells are found, in all cases, around scattered vessels in the posterior columns and near the diseased pyramidal tracts in two cases. Some fat-bearing cells are also free in the tissue near the most affected parts.

The blood vessels in one case are quite conspicuous. While no new blood vessel formation is in progress, the smaller arteries and arterioles appear to have increased and the subendothelial connective tissue of most of them appears to have thickened. The vessels of the meninges show slight thickening of the intima and media in two cases.

Figure 20
Gliosis of anterior
white commissure
in eighth decade.
Holzer stain

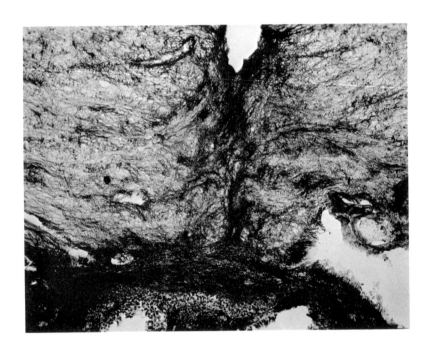

Ninth Decade

There is only one case in this group and the picture, as a whole, is a further accentuation of that seen in the seventh and eighth decades. The dura is thick and fibrous. The leptomeninges are free from infiltration but are moderately thickened by an overgrowth of swollen, collagenous bands. The arteries are sclerotic (Fig. 21).

The white matter is porous, especially around the edge and the posterior columns are edematous in all levels. The gray matter is edematous and the perivascular and pericellular spaces are moderately dilated. There are no perivascular infiltrations. The central canal has the customary collection of proliferated ependymal cells. Corpora amylacea are found at all levels, particularly near the entering posterior roots, but the number is not excessive.

The nerve cells of the anterior horns are hyperchromatic. The nuclei are often darkened, and sometimes folds occur in the nuclear membranes. Many of the cell bodies are shrunken, especially in the medial groups, and most of the remaining cells are swollen and distorted by lipochrome. The Nissl granules are often pyknotic and are either clumped around the edge or arranged in bizarre shapes and patterns overlying the lipochrome, with sharp spicules of Nissl substance interspersed among bigger globules. The lipochrome, sometimes vacuolar, is abundant and often reaches 85 per cent of the cell volume. Some cells have undergone practically complete pigmentary atrophy with scarcely anything but lipofuchsin left. Even the smaller cells of the posterior horns often show as much as 50 per cent lipochrome. The lateral horn cells are swollen and rounded with eccentric nuclei that make them resemble the "fish-eye" cells of axonal reaction. A few of the cells are elongated and wavy. The nuclei are dark and have multifolded membranes. The Nissl substance is irregular; some cells show chromatolysis while others show heavy, coarse granules. The lipochrome usually appears in a single mass at one pole or at the center, occupying as much as 80 per cent of the cell volume. Similarly, in Clarke's column the cell bodies are often distorted by abundant lipochrome. The nuclei are eccentric and dark and the Nissl granules, when not clumped close to the nucleus, are pyknotic and peripheral, indicating a large amount of central chromatolysis.

The Weigert picture shows more pronounced thinning and paling in this cord than in those of earlier decades. In this case even the anterior columns show slight thinning. Thinning is more marked in the lateral

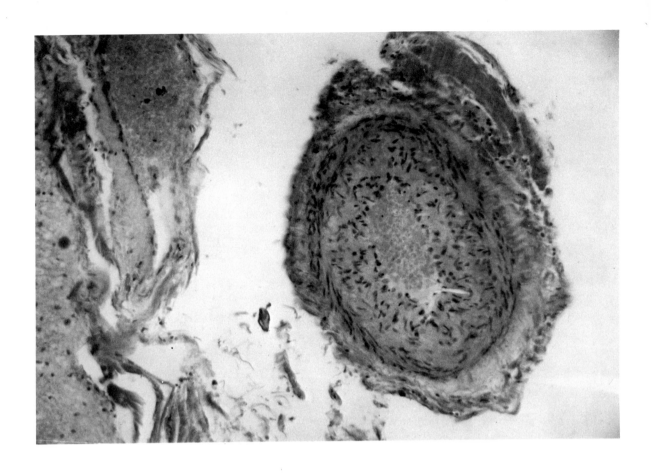

Figure 21
Arteriosclerosis of
anterior spinal artery
at 82 years.
H & E stain

columns and most conspicuous of all in the posterior columns. It can be seen to best advantage at the cervical level, where the degenerated axons in Goll's and Burdach's columns are separated by a band of relatively healthy myelinated tissue. In other words, the fibers from the legs and arms are degenerated but the fibers from the trunk are relatively normal. High power magnification shows plenty of swollen and fragmented sheaths, together with many myelin figures. These can be seen to a lesser extent in the posterior roots (Fig. 22).

The Bodian impregnation shows, on cross section, some swelling of axons in the posterior and lateral columns and a little around the edge. There are many swollen sheaths and some empty sheath spaces, especially in the posterior columns. Some tan bodies are present in the conventional loci at both the cervical and the lumbar level. The longitudinal sections show granular fragmentation.

The generalized increase in glial cells in both the gray and the white matter is seen to best advantage in Goll's column close to the raphe. Some of these cells are oligodendroglia but the majority are astrocytes. Both are hyperchromatic, but especially the astrocytes. Identical pairs of daughter cells are often visible, and a good many perivascular glia can be found. No examples of neuronophagia can be found, but occasional glial nodules are seen in the anterior horns at the cervical and lumbar

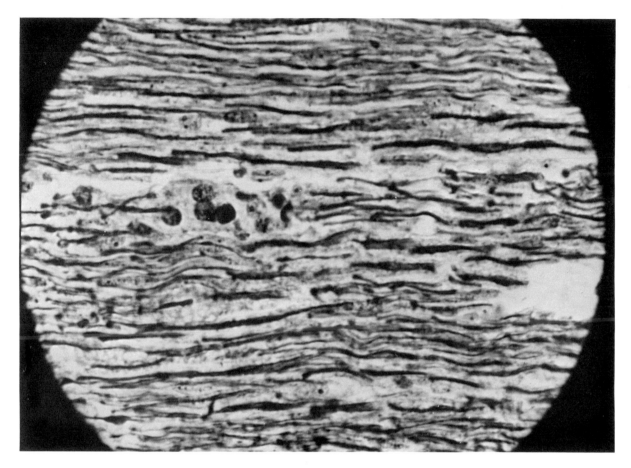

levels. The Holzer stain shows a slight perivascular gliosis, a strong anterior horn gliosis, and a dense gliosis in Goll's column.

The fat stain shows a picture similar to that of the eighth decade except that the intracellular pigment in the anterior horn cells is not as bright red as might be expected. There are many fat-laden perivascular gitter cells, and when a vessel is cut longitudinally they can be seen in long rows in the same profusion. Few fatty masses are found loose in the tissue.

Diffuse hyperplasia of the walls of the blood vessels is conspicuous in the meninges as well as in the cord tissue. The anterior spinal artery, as well as the smaller arteries on either side of the central canal, shows a distinct diminution of the size of the lumen.

Figure 22
Posterior root alterations
in axons at 82 years.
Bodian stain

Discussion

The histological variations in the so-called normal spinal cord can be divided into two main groups: those that are associated with general systemic disease and those that are the natural result of advancing age. The lesions of both groups, while positive enough, are presumably mild, since their signs are not usually detected in the ordinary physical examination. The lesions of the former group can be of practically any type and may involve any or all types of brain tissues. Their pathogenesis is variable and has to be determined separately in each case: thus, in septicemia minute pericapillary foci of softening, with fatty degeneration of axons and myelin and small clusters of microglia, are found in abundance; while in uremia the lesion is most clearly indicated in the nerve cells by marked chromatolysis. The action is embolic in one instance and "toxic" in the other. On the other hand, while every case does not fall completely into its chronological niche, because some people age faster or more slowly than others, a framework of order can be made out in which the degree of pathological variation can be, at least partly, correlated with advancing age. Some structures fit into the pattern more consistently than others, for senile changes depend not only on the effects produced by general systemic alterations outside the spinal cord, but also on the effects produced by one structure upon another within the cord itself. For that reason abrupt generalizations are impossible and different structures like the meninges, the myelin, the axons, the nerve cells, the glia, and the blood vessels will have to be considered separately.

There is a generalized increase in thickness of the meninges with advancing age, as Rokitansky[11] first pointed out. The dura is more consistent than the pia-arachnoid in this respect, for it is nearly always thickened in later years and is rarely affected in earlier years without neurological disease. The soft meninges, however, while usually exhibiting a collagenous overgrowth in the later decades, often show thickening earlier in life as well. The pia-arachnoid varies in thickness not only from one decade to another and from cord to cord within each decade, but also from one level to another in the same cord. Sometimes it may even show a difference between the dorsal and ventral surfaces at the same level. The delicate, filamentous strands described by Weed[15] are rarely seen; denser bands of collagen are usually found even in the earliest decades of life. An inflammatory reaction is indicated by the presence of lymphocytes and plasma cells and a few polymorphonuclears and macrophages. This is too mild to be called a true meningitis, since the number of cells found within the circumference of any one section is usually between 30 and 50. Nevertheless, these infiltrating cells may be sufficiently stimulating to cause a proliferation of fibroblasts and hence a collagenous thickening. Infiltration is found in seven of the thirty-one cords in the present series, usually in the neighborhood of the entering posterior roots or the blood vessels, especially the anterior spinal artery. While thickening of the pia-arachnoid occurs in many other cases, it is present in all but one of these seven. In that one there is no thickening, but the patient may have died too soon for it to have occurred. In some of the cords which show thickening but no infiltration, the inflammation may simply have undergone resolution, leaving a collagenous scar. But the fibroblastic and collagenous proliferation cannot be attributed to an underlying, subclinical inflammation in every case. In most instances this mild infiltration of the pia-arachnoid is accompanied by a similarly mild perivascular reaction within the cord tissue. The blood vessels of the gray matter are the ones most commonly involved, although occasionally the white matter shows the same reaction. The majority of the cells are lymphocytes, although plasma cells occasionally appear; the groups are small—usually six or seven to a single cuff. These cells are always found in the Virchow-Robin space (never out in the parenchymatous tissue), and their presence bears no relation to the presence or absence of fat-laden perivascular gitter cells. Sometimes a meningeal reaction occurs without this mild myelitis, and sometimes the latter occurs without any meningeal inflammation, but in any event the only importance of such an infiltration lies in its relation to other things. The inflammation itself is so mild as to be subclinical, but if it can stimulate the production of fibroblasts it may later have pathological if not clinical significance.

In the zone of Redlich-Obersteiner (Figs. 23 A–B) the pia-arachnoid crowds up around the entering posterior root in most cases where there is leptomeningeal thickening. In some instances the thickened connective-tissue strands extend peripherally among the entering fibers, and in a few cases they extend centrally beyond the pial line in the direction of the posterior horns. Occasionally the nerve roots are constricted, but it cannot be said definitely that this is pathological, for a natural constriction occurs in this zone. However, it seems obvious that in this region, where the myelin sheath is diminished, the relatively unprotected axons are easy prey to the overgrowth of connective tissue.

Nests of arachnoid cells like those which Weed referred to as serving as bases for calcification and ossification were not encountered in the present series. Calcification, a common finding in the meninges of old people according to some authors,[14] was found only twice—and then in the form of flat discs about half a centimeter in diameter. These discs were enmeshed in the arachnoid and freely movable over the surface of the cord. Farther down over the cauda equina, calcified plaques were firmly bound to the root fibers, but the binding was not tight enough to cause any appreciable constriction of the nerve fibers.

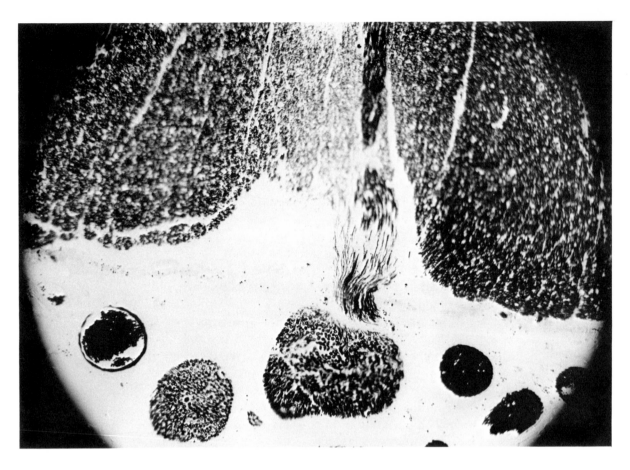

Figure 23A
Zone of Redlich-Obersteiner.
Weigert stain

Only in the very youngest cases, and in older cases where shrinkage has occurred, can the cord be said to be relatively free from edema. In all the other cases a loose consistence to the cord structure and dilatation of the perivascular and pericellular spaces indicate the presence of fluid in the cord tissue. This is especially noticeable around the periphery, where a porous condition is often present. The fact that the youngest cases are relatively free from this loose, porous condition indicates that artifact is not responsible for dilated pericellular and perivascular spaces and spongy white matter, as some authors contend.* While there are some swollen oligodendroglia in the white matter of these edematous cases, most of the swelling is extracellular, the nerve cells showing no liquefaction. The white matter is more affected than the gray, as is usual in edema.[16]

The central canal is patent in cords of the earliest decades, being lined by a single layer of ependymal cells. By the third decade, however, subependymal cells begin to proliferate and clusters of these lining cells, together with other types of glia, form conspicuous nests in the gray commissure. Reduplication of the central canal itself and outlying clusters of fat-laden ependymal cells stippled with bright red granules are

---

* One must be aware, moreover, that artifacts are sometimes caused by removing cords before fixation.

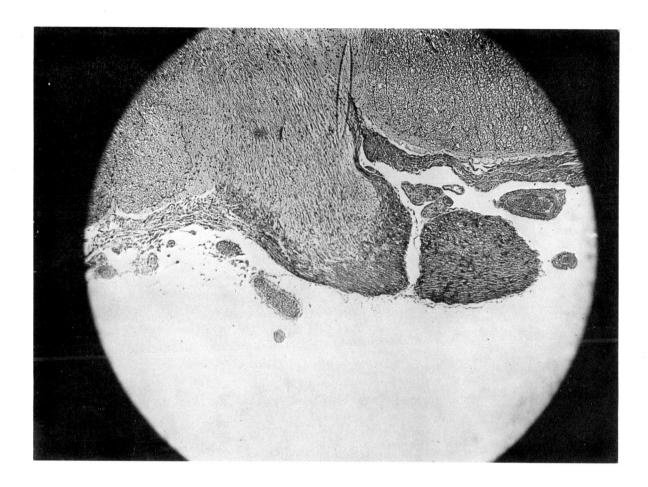

common findings especially in the cords of older people. These changes
are quite pronounced but apparently have no significance except as regressive glial phenomena. The glial nests show no degeneration, and
the line can always be drawn between them and syringomyelia.

The Weigert preparations show at a glance that more or less serious
myelin loss occurs with advancing age in the various columns of the
cord. This is most conspicuous in the posterior columns, but lateral
column loss and thinning and paling around the periphery are also consistent findings. If the cords are grouped according to age decades, there
is a sequence of development of myelin loss in the posterior columns
from the fourth through the ninth decade. Not every cord fits exactly
into the group corresponding to its age, because of more severe or less
severe myelin loss. In fact, approximately one-third of the cords showed
no correlation between the degree of myelin loss and the age group to
which they belonged. For example, one cord of the second decade (the
lupus erythematosus case) had as much myelin loss as the customary
fifth-decade group and one cord of the sixth decade showed no more degeneration than is usually found in the fourth decade. Even though the
cords are grouped according to age sequence, it is obvious that factors
other than the mere passage of time are responsible for the alterations in

Figure 23B
Zone of Redlich-Obersteiner.
Van Gieson stain

43

the myelin. Canavan[17] believed that vitamin deficiency and related anemia are partly responsible for myelin loss in the spinal cord. The cords she examined were from patients suffering from mental disease who had lived in institutions for a good many years. Such a combination of circumstances might well lead to a vitamin deficiency because of poor appetite due to confinement, monotonous diet, and food fads based on paranoid notions. Some of her illustrations also suggest the probability of pernicious anemia and the possibility of ergotism,[18] not only because of the distribution of the lesions but also because of the porous, punched-out appearance of the white matter. While some of the cords in the present series had myelin lesions like Canavan's, most of them did not. In a few cases there was a distinct honeycombing, especially around the periphery, but in most instances the myelin loss was smooth and regular and the tissue destruction was incomplete, leaving pale areas but no holes.

As has been pointed out, this myelin loss was found in the lateral columns in the region of the pyramidal tracts and also around the periphery, but it was most consistently found in the posterior columns. Neurologists have known for a long time that patients over fifty years old frequently show diminished vibratory sense and varying degrees of ataxia. Corbin and Gardner[19] demonstrated that the number of myelinated fibers diminishes with age and that lesions occur in the entering posterior roots, even before the spinal cord is reached. They found that approximately 1 per cent of the fibers degenerated before the third decade and that in cords of the ninth decade there were 32 per cent fewer fibers in the posterior roots at the eighth and ninth thoracic levels than there were in cords of the third decade. In the present series a fairly consistent relation was also noted between degeneration of the posterior root fibers and posterior column disease—particularly in the fibers from the arms and legs, where degeneration is apt to be more conspicuous. Corbin's and Gardner's counts were made on thoracic sections but Figure 22 shows that the fibers from the trunk degenerate relatively less than those from the arms and legs. In 1903 Ingbert[20] pointed out that there is a close relation between the number of fibers in the posterior roots and the spinal section from which they come and also that there are fewer fascicles and smaller nerve fibers in the small posterior roots than in the large posterior roots. It therefore follows that, even if there were as much degeneration in the posterior roots of the thoracic region as in those of the cervical and lumbar regions, the corresponding cord degeneration would not be so conspicuous.

The vascular supply of the cord[8, 21] is designed in such a way[22] that the periphery is less copiously supplied with a capillary bed than the deeper parts of the cord, and Canavan[17] believes that the poor blood supply near the edge helps to account for the spongy degeneration of the peripheral myelin. This may be so, but in the present series peripheral degeneration is found even in some of the youngest cords and in a good many others in which there is no evidence of vascular disease. In cases

44

with detectable arteriosclerosis in the parenchyma, as well as in the vessels of the pia, perivascular demyelination is also found within the cord substance. Such perivascular demyelination is always accompanied by peripheral degeneration.

The pyramidal tract is not so often or so conspicuously involved as the columns of Goll and Burdach, nevertheless it is definitely degenerated in a good many of the older cords. One need seek no further for an explanation of the pyramidal tract involvement if the lesions were of the type found in combined-system disease. But in the present series the lesions are usually of a different sort. The diseased pyramidal tracts are gliosed, although less often than the posterior column tracts. In combined-system disease gliosis does not take place except in treated cases. The brains were not examined in this series, but it is well known that in old age small spots of cellular gray matter (pale areas) are scattered throughout the central cortex of the frontal lobe.[14] Such cortical cell loss might account for the thinning and paling of the pyramidal tracts.

In one or two instances diseased myelin is found in the posterior columns at the lumbar level, while the posterior column tracts remain relatively normal at the thoracic and cervical levels. It can only be assumed that merely the myelin, and not the axon is degenerated, even though a fairly dense lumbar gliosis is seen in the Holzer stain, for it is not likely that short (intersegmental) fibers were degenerated.

Zimmerman[23] has shown that not only the cord but also the posterior roots and, to a lesser extent, the anterior roots are involved in vitamin A deficiency experimentally produced in animals, and he believes that the sensory tract changes in the cord follow those of the posterior root. But there again the question of gliosis comes in. Does posterior column gliosis follow vitamin A deficiency? As pointed out above, the thickening of the pia-arachnoid in advancing age and the impinging of this thickened structure on posterior roots in the vulnerable zone of Redlich-Obersteiner must also be considered. If vitamin deficiency alone were involved, the anterior roots should be affected with equal severity. In the present series of spinal cords this did not occur.

That does not mean, however, that the anterior roots escaped all disease. While severe myelin lesions are easily detected in the peripheral nerves, the criteria for mild disease are by no means well established. There is a great variation in the size of the medullated fibers of the spinal roots at all levels of the normal cord, and so size in itself is of no help. Wolbach and his co-workers[24] have shown that the fine honeycombing that is often seen between the incisura of Schmidt-Lantermann in supposedly normal nerves is in reality a very early sign of myelin degeneration. Although such a porous condition is often encountered in the anterior roots, more advanced changes in the myelin are not particularly common or conspicuous. However, the axons themselves undergo changes, especially when they have just left the cells but are still in the cord substance. This is indicated by the fact that swollen, hyalin-like fragments of axons (referred to above as tan bodies) are sometimes found in cords of the early decades as well as in those of the late decades. Their limitation to the cervical and lumbar levels accords with the pattern of myelin degeneration within the cord as seen in Figure 19. These are the axons of motor cells and the fragments are found close to the cell bodies. As no correspondence is found between the presence of tan bodies and axonal reaction in the anterior horn, it can be reasoned that the lesions result from a degenerative process rather than a deficiency and that the muscular atrophy met with in old age has a neurological component. Tan bodies are set aside from other spinal root lesions by their selective location in the valley between the anteromedial and anterolateral cell groups at the cervical and lumbar levels and by their unvarying size, consistency, and argentophilic reaction. On longitudinal section the intensity of the axonal disease appears scarcely more severe in the latest decades than it is in the other decades after forty, even though the myelin loss is far greater. That is because the diseased axons are phagocytosed as the years go by, leaving no trace of their remains, while the Weigert is a negative picture and shows the accumulated myelin loss.

In the anterior horns several types of nerve cell disease were encountered. Acute swelling, axonal reaction, ischemic and chronic shrinkage, abiotrophy, and pigmentary atrophy were the types most commonly met. Axonal reaction occurred at almost any age but most often between the fifth and the seventh decade. When the axonal reaction type of cells contained vacuoles, it was difficult to distinguish them from the acute swelling type, for in neither case do the glia respond to an accompanying reaction. But the acute, cloudy swelling is of an agonal nature, or at least of short duration, while the axonal reaction is of long standing. Ischemic shrinkage occurs at any age and so does so-called chronic shrinkage. Here also were cells reacting in either of these two ways unaccompanied by glial responses. Abiotrophy was occasionally encountered. In this condition the cells become pale, sometimes acidophilic, then fade more and more. After a while only a suggestion of their presence remains, then they finally disappear.

Pigmentary atrophy in which the lipofuchsin of the cell increases at the expense of the Nissl and other intracellular substance, was the most consistent finding. The lipoid pigment increases to such dimensions that the nucleus is pushed to one side and the cell distorted with only a thin rim of cytoplasm remaining. Sometimes, in fact, only the lipochrome is left, the cell having disappeared. While lipofuchsin is occasionally seen as a pale, scanty pigment before the third or fourth decade, its presence after that remains constant, although in a fat stain it is only pink or rusty brick-red. True atrophy begins later. This pigmentary atrophy is most severe in old age, when the lipoid becomes fat and takes a bright red stain.

In regard to shrinkage of the cells with advancing years, it may be

46

said that some old cords show dense, markedly concave cell bodies with dark hyperchromatic processes (that is, chronic shrinkage) rather than the swelling and distortion due to excessive lipochrome. Shrinkage of the nerve cells of the senile and senescent spinal cord is not so common as one might expect from similar lesions in the cortex in senility.[25] In fact, if the actual measurements of the cell diameters are any criterion, the cell bodies are larger and more voluminous in old than in young cords. The average dimensions of a cell in the anterolateral group at the cervical level of a man in the ninth decade are 54 x 29 micra, while a corresponding cell in a sixteen-year-old girl measures 43 x 22 micra. The difference is largely due to lipochrome, which often occupies from 75 to 90 per cent of the cell volume in the older cord. Shrinkage of nerve cells deprived of their lipochrome results in hyperchromatic, tortuous processes.

No Alzheimer cells, nor any other cells with evidence of intracellular fibrillary disease, were encountered. Normally, the cells of Clarke's column have a large amount of lipochrome and in youth the Nissl substance is distributed regularly over this pigment. As longevity increases the lipofuchsin becomes more conspicuous and the discrete Nissl granules become pulverized at first in a central and later in a generalized chromatolysis. Eventually the cell bodies become distorted and the nuclei eccentric. This resembles true axonal reaction and is probably the result of disease of the direct spino-cerebellar tract on the periphery of the cord. No similar reaction was noted, however, in the cells of the posterior horns.

The lateral horn cells are of the stichochrome type, but their variations are so numerous that one may classify them only with great caution. They vary not only in size and shape but also in number. No correspondence was found between their alterations and age. Swelling, chromatolysis, fatty degeneration, and often shrunken cells with long, wavy, tortuous processes (Fig. 10) occur unsystematically throughout the series without particular reference to age or to type of illness. The number of cells in the lateral horns is quite inconstant and often differs considerably on the two sides. Replacement gliosis, such as that reported by Orton and Bender[26] in acrodynia and pernicious anemia, is often present in the older cords of the present series. It is not specifically localized as it was in Orton's cases but merely a part of generalized gray matter gliosis. With the exception of Stilling's nucleus and the cells of the posterior horn, the nerve cells of the spinal cord are normally unaccompanied by satellites. Neuronophagia was practically never found in this series of cases and what might be called satellitosis was only found occasionally. Once in a while a small glial nodule of oligodendrocytes was encountered in the gray matter in what was evidently the site of former nerve cells. These glial nodules are no more conspicuous in old age than in youth and are probably the result of some relatively acute process. Gliosis occurs in the anterior horns (Fig. 16 b) but how much is due to involutional changes in the glia and how much to scar replace-

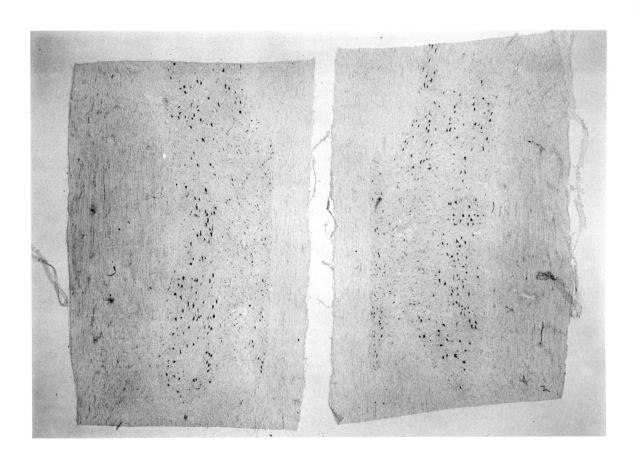

ment of nerve cells it is difficult to say. The widespread loss of nerve cells in an acute disease like poliomyelitis is easily detected not only by direct observation but also by inference from the glial scar. In a gradual, long-drawn-out process like aging, where there is no widespread loss of nerve cells in the cord and where there is no neuronophagia to mark the site of cell destruction, the most reliable method of determining cell loss is by actually counting the cells.

The technique of cell-counting is full of pitfalls. Laruelle and Reumont[27] have shown that in plurisegmental, longitudinal sections unilateral cell losses can be rather easily discerned for matching columns of cells. But this technique does not permit studying all columns in one section. The longitudinal section illustrated in Figure 24 shows how easily one can be misled in studying cross sections. Because of the condensation of cells at the segmental levels and the relative sparcity of cells between segments, each block has to be cut squarely across to get comparative pictures on both sides. Moreover, in comparing different levels of the same cord one must always cut at the same relative level in each segment. Then, as for the actual counting: How large should a fragment of cell be to be included in the count? Must it include the nucleus or only enough cytoplasm to identify it as a nerve cell? These are the main reasons why cell counts were not made.

48

The normal spinal cord (that is, the cord in which there is no obvious nerve cell or tract degeneration and in which the interstitial tissues are in a "resting" state) contains oligodendroglia, astrocytes, and microglia. Hassin[6] implied in 1940 that the normal cord contains no microglia and subsequently[28] stated that the normal cord not only has no microglia but also no astrocytes. Although it is difficult to stain microglia and even astrocytes in the cord with specific methods while they are in the resting stage, it seems extreme to deny their presence. Is there a sharp line of demarcation between brain and cord when astrocytes and microglia are present and when they are absent? Possibly the discrepancy between Hassin's findings and those of most other workers lies in the definition of what constitutes a normal cord. Certainly if hyperchromatosis, in itself, is taken to be a sign of cell activity,[29] then there were no normal cords in this series, for in every single case something could be found, after diligent searching, that indicated the past or present progress of pathological activity. Obviously these minor alterations have to be interpreted in the light of other findings. As far as this series is concerned microglia and astrocytes are present in every single case. Silver and gold preparations were only made to elucidate special points of interest, but it is maintained that even in Nissl preparations the various glia cells can be identified.

Oligodendroglia react separately or in small groups, but when they are affected in widespread areas the change is secondary to some other reaction. In both gray and white matter the swelling of oligodendroglia is a commonplace finding. While it may be a post mortem autolytic change,[30] or a change associated with edema,[31] there is little evidence that it represents a stage in phagocytosis. In spite of the work of Cramer and Alpers,[5] active phagocytosis by oligodendroglia, in the sense of mobile macrophages and gitter cell formation, was not observed. It is true that perineuronal satellites of oligodendroglia occasionally appeared in the anterior horns where none normally exist, but it is not quite clear whether this represented true motility or proximation due to extension from hyperplasia. It is possible that a slight amount of motility may be managed by oligodendroglia. Also, in a few instances the oligodendroglia seem to be participating in the destruction of dead anterior horn cells. Here again it is maintained that this is a process of adsorption rather than phagocytosis and may be included under the heading of "fixed *Abbau*" because these oligodendroglia do not migrate away to the perivascular spaces but remain at least for some time on the site of the former ganglion. In fact, this minute cluster of oligodendroglia is to a limited extent fiber-forming and the glial nodule is a small scar. It is not maintained that the arrangement represents a true metaplasia from oligodendroglia to fibrillary macroglia, although this may possibly be so, but rather that oligodendroglia are capable of being developed into an intermediary type between their resting stage and astrocytes. Later on, these glial nuclei, like many astrocytic nuclei, disappear from the scar or at least disperse from their clustered arrangement. In older cords, where there is a relatively small loss of anterior horn cells and a compensating astro-gliosis, these glial nodules are not conspicuous in the Holzer stain.

In disease of the white matter the oligodendrocytic picture is not always the same. Sometimes, when there is loss of myelin, the remaining sheaths seem to be more closely compressed and the glial nuclei consequently look denser. Sometimes either the sheaths remain separated or there is an oligocytopenia, for the oligodendroglial nuclei are noticeably sparser. There is no obvious correspondence between the relative density of these nuclei and the intensity of gliosis.

To complete the discussion of oligodendroglia, the corpora amylacea should be mentioned. Ferraro and Damon[32] have shown that corpora amylacea are derived, at least partially, from oligodendroglia. They made their deductions from silver preparations. As has been observed by other authors, the corpora amylacea increase greatly with the age of the patient, and in some cases they become extremely dense. Their distribution suggests the origin that Ferraro and Damon have attributed to them, for they are arranged rather like interfascicular oligodendroglia and they cease sharply where Schwann cells begin. It is true that astrocytes have this same distribution but they are much less numerous.

Microglia are encountered in every case, and even when arranged in small pericapillary clusters, they often retain their rod-like nuclei and have processes free from swellings. They are present in both the gray and white matter and perform their usual function of active phagocytosis. Fat-laden gitter cells and intermediary forms are found free in the cord tissue and also in the perivascular spaces. They are only slightly more numerous in the oldest decades than they are at any time after middle life, because the myelin and axons degenerate at an almost steady rate, speeding up very little in old age.

The astrocytes proliferate throughout the white matter wherever there is a myelin loss. Hyperchromatosis and hyperplasia are obvious and, even in the nonspecific stains, extensive processes and daughter cells are often visible. Plump astrocytes (*gemästete Zellen*)[29] are rarely encountered, however, and most of the hypertrophic forms are of the simple granular variety. When the myelin lesion is patchy, small foci of gliosis are correspondingly present. If perivascular demyelination is present, as in some of the older cords, perivascular proliferations of macroglia can be seen. Sometimes they are so dense that their pedicles show up clearly as the membrana gliosa limitans.

In addition to these small foci of gliosis, larger and denser fields appear in the posterior columns and to a lesser extent in the lateral columns and around the periphery. Usually, we found that the older the cord the denser the gliosis, but, occasionally as with myelin loss, the reaction is well advanced in some of the younger cords.

In addition to replacement of myelin by gliosis, the Holzer picture shows a denser gliosis in the gray matter with increased age. This is especially conspicuous in the anterior horns and the posterior commissure.

Replacement of cell loss by gliosis in the anterior horns is not the entire answer here, because the cell loss due to old age is slight and the gliosis extends through the gray commissure to the boundary between the gray and white matter where there are no nerve cells. As pointed out some time ago by Bertrand,[33] the glia undergo an involution under certain circumstances. A protoplasmic astrocyte may become fibrous (in premature senility) and a fibrous astrocyte may become "ameboid" (degeneration). These regressive changes are seen in the present series of cords. Many fibrous astrocytes put in an appearance in the later decades and many of the glia close to the central canal—ependymal cells as well as more differentiated astrocytes—undergo granular and fatty degeneration. In accounting for this gray matter gliosis, the involutionary changes in the interstitial tissue should not be overstressed, for in the white matter the correspondence between the location of gliosis and the location of myelin loss is exact enough to enable one to infer a cause and effect relationship. In the anterior horns the cell loss must be kept in mind, because in chronic as well as in acute cell loss, such as one finds in poliomyelitis, glial scars remain. These scars are not limited to the exact nests where the nerve cells used to be, but extend beyond them in all directions and probably cause some contraction of the gray matter.

Arteriosclerosis of the spinal cord is a relatively rare condition. As mentioned by Hamilton[13] and others, it sometimes occurs but is usually mild. As the intima thickens in old age there is a corresponding narrowing of the lumina. Sometimes the media also thickens but even less often than the intima. No calcification was found in the present series. In a few cords the elastica was split at certain levels of the anterior spinal artery. In one or two cords a proliferation of blood vessels was noted, especially in the posterior and lateral columns. As mentioned above, the cords of patients with obvious vascular disease showed peripheral demyelination and gliosis.

Alzheimer cells and senile placques, those two classic signs of cortical pathology in senile dementia, are not found in old spinal cords. The pathological findings in old spinal cords are more analagous to the cortical lesions of simple senility without dementia.

To summarize:

1. Thirty-one spinal cords from nonneurological patients were studied histologically.

2. The lesions were of two types: those derived from intercurrent disease and those that resulted from advancing age.

3. The lesions resulting from nonneurological disease are mild, spotty, and inconstant but definite enough to be considered in any histological study of spinal cords. They mostly affect nerve cells, but sometimes glia, myelin, axons, and blood vessels are also involved.

4. Lesions resulting from advancing age first begin, as constant findings, about the fourth decade and in a general way increase in severity through the rest of life. These lesions involve all the structures of the cord and are widespread and often systematic.

5. The pathogenesis of the lesions is not always clear but various theories as to the origin of both categories have been considered and discussed.

References

References Cited

1. BRUCE, A. *A Topographical Atlas of the Spinal Cord.* Williams & Norgate, London, 1901

2. NISSL, F. Kritische Fragen der Nervenzellen-Anatomie; Antwort auf Benda's Aufsatz in Nr. 17 (Jahrg. 1895) dieses Blattes. *Neurol. Centralbl.* (Leipzig), 15:98–103, 1896

3. TILNEY, F., AND RILEY, H. A. *The Form and Functions of the Central Nervous System; an Introduction to the Study of Nervous Diseases,* 2d ed. Hoeber, New York, 1923

4. JAKOB, A. "Ueber die feinere Histologie der sekundären Faserdegeneration in der weissen Substanz des Rückenmarks (mit besonderer Berücksichtigung der Abbauvorgänge)" in: Nissl, F., and Alzheimer, A. *Histologische und Histopathologische Arbeiten über die Grosshirnrinde mit besonderer Berücksichtigung der pathologischen Anatomie der Geisteskrankheiten,* vol. 5, pp. 1–181. Fischer, Jena, 1913

5. CRAMER, F., AND ALPERS, B. J. The functions of the glia in secondary degeneration of the spinal cord; the oligodendroglia as phagocytes, *Arch. Path.,* 13:23–55, Jan. 1932

6. HASSIN, G. B. *Histopathology of the Peripheral and Central Nervous Systems.* William Wood, Baltimore, 1933

7. ADAMKIEWICZ, A. Die Blutgefässe des menschlichen Rückenmarkes; I—Die Gefässe der Rückenmarkssubstanz, *Sitzungsb. Akad. Wissen. Wien,* Math.-nat. Kl., Abt. 3, 84:469–502, 1881

8. ROSS, J. Distribution of the arteries of the spinal cord, *Brain,* 3:80–84, 1880

9. WEBBER, S. G. "The pathological histology of the spinal cord [with a short introduction on the normal histology]" in: *Medical and Surgical Reports of the City Hospital of the City of Boston,* 3d series, pp. 1–33. Boston, 1882

10. CAMPBELL, A. W. The morbid changes in the cerebro-spinal nervous system of the aged insane, *J. Ment. Sc.* (London), 40:638–649, 1894

11. ROKITANSKY, C. *A Manual of Pathological Anatomy* (trans. from the last German edition), vol. 3. Blanchard & Lea, Philadelphia, 1855

12. CHARCOT, J. M. *Clinical Lectures on Senile and Chronic Diseases* (trans. by W. S. Tuke). New Sydenham Soc., London, 1881

13. HAMILTON, A. S. A study of the senile spinal cord in cases of mental disease, *Boston Med. & Surg. J.,* 163:189–196, 1910

14. CRITCHLEY, M. Neurology of old age (Goulstonian lecture), *Lancet,* 1:1119–1127, May 23, 1931

15. WEED, L. H. "The meninges; with special reference to the cell coverings of the leptomeninges," in: Penfield, W. (ed.), *Cytology and Cellular Pathology of the Nervous System*, vol. 2, pp. 611–634. Hoeber, New York, 1932

16. STEWART-WALLACE, A. M. A biochemical study of cerebral tissue, and of changes in cerebral oedema, *Brain*, 62:426–438, Dec. 1939

17. CANAVAN, M. Lesions in the spinal cord in mental disease and defect recognized by myelin sheath stain; report of 600 unselected cases with appendix on technic, *J. M. A. Georgia*, 28:324–331, Aug. 1939

18. TUCZEK, F. Ueber die Veränderungen im Centralnervensystem, Speziell in den Hintersträngen des Rückenmarks, bei Ergotismus, *Arch. Psychiat.* (Berlin), 13:99–154, 1882

19. CORBIN, K., AND GARDNER, E. D. Decrease in the number of myelinated fibers in human spinal roots with age, *Anat. Rec.*, 68:63–74, April 25, 1937

20. INGBERT, C. An enumeration of the medullated nerve fibers in the dorsal roots of the spinal nerves of man, *J. Comp. Neurol.* (Granville, O.), 13:53–120, 1903

21. ADAMKIEWICZ, A. Die Blutgefässe des menschlichen Rückenmarkes; II—Die Gefässe der Rückenmarksoberfläche, *Sitzungsb. Akad. Wissen. Wien*, Math.-nat. Kl., Abt. 3, 85:101–130, 1882

22. TUREEN, L. L. "Circulation of the spinal cord and the effect of vascular occlusion," Chapter XVII in Assn. for Research in Nervous and Mental Diseases, vol. 18—*The Circulation of the Brain and Spinal Cord; a Symposium on Blood Supply* (Proc. of the assn., 1937). Williams & Wilkins, Baltimore, 1938

23. ZIMMERMAN, H. M. Lesions of the nervous system in vitamin deficiency; rats on a diet low in vitamin A., *J. Exper. Med.*, 57:215–228, Feb. 1933

24. WOLBACH, S. B. AND BESSEY, O. A. Vitamin A deficiency and the nervous system, *Arch. Path.*, 32:689–727, 1941

25. SIMCHOWICZ, T. "Histologische Studien über die senile Demenz," in: Nissl, F., and Alzheimer, A. *Histologische und Histopathologische Arbeiten über die Grosshirnrinde mit besonderer Berücksichtigung der pathologischen Anatomie der Geisteskrankheiten*, vol. 4, pp. 267–444. Fischer, Jena, 1911

26. ORTON, S. T., AND BENDER, L. Lesions in lateral horns of the spinal cord in acrodynia, pellagra, and pernicious anemia, *Bull. Neurol. Inst., N.Y.*, 1:506–531, Nov. 1931

27. LARUELLE, L., AND REUMONT, M. Etude de l'anatomie microscopique de la moelle épinière par la méthode des coupes longitudinales plurisegmentaires, *Ann. anat. path. méd-chir.*, 10:1130–1141, Nov. 1933

28. HASSIN, G. B. Amyotrophic lateral sclerosis; anatomic and pathologic considerations, *Arch. Neurol. & Psychiat.*, 43:765–777, 1940; correction: 43:1056, 1940

29. SPIELMEYER, W. *Histopathologie des Nervensystems*. Springer, Berlin, 1922

30. PENFIELD, W., AND CONE, M. The acute regressive changes of neuroglia (amoeboid glia and acute swelling of oligodendroglia), *J. f. Psychol. u. Neurol.*, 34:204–220, 1926

31. FERRARO, A. The reaction of the brain tissue to intravenous injection of hypotonic solutions, *J. Nerv. & Ment. Dis.*, 71:129–144, Feb. 1930

32. FERRARO, A., AND DAMON, L. A. Histogenesis of amyloid bodies in the central nervous system, *Arch. Path.,* 12:229–244, Aug. 1931

33. BERTRAND, I. G. *Les Processus de Désintégration Nerveuse.* Masson, Paris, 1923

34. DEJERINE, J., AND ANDRÉ-THOMAS, *Maladies de la moelle épinière* (Nouveau Traité de médecine et de thérapeutique, vol. 34). Baillière, Paris, 1909

35. STREETER, G. L. The status of metamerism in the central nervous system of chick embryos, *J. Comp. Neurol.,* 57:455–475, June 1933

36. ELLIOTT, H. C. Studies on the motor cells of the spinal cord; I—Distribution in the normal human cord, *Am. J. Anat.,* 70:95–117, 1942

    ——— Studies on the motor cells of the spinal cord; II—Distribution in the normal human fetal cord, *Am. J. Anat.,* 72:29–38, 1943

    ——— Studies on the motor cells of the spinal cord; III—Position and extent of lesions in the nuclear pattern of convalescent and chronic poliomyelitis patients, *Am. J. Path.,* 21:87–97, 1945

    ——— Cross-sectional diameters and areas of the human spinal cord, *Anat. Rec.,* 93:287–293, 1945

37. WEIL, A. *Textbook of Neuropathology,* 2d ed. Grune & Stratton, New York, 1945

38. CONEL, J. LER. *The Postnatal Development of the Human Cerebral Cortex;* vol. III—*The Cortex of the Three-Month Infant.* Harvard Univ. Press, Cambridge, 1947

Other References

Not referred to in detail, but used as a background for the study.

CHARCOT, J. M. *Lectures on the Localisation of Cerebral and Spinal Diseases, Delivered at the Faculty of Medicine of Paris* (trans. and ed. by W. B. Hadden), New Sydenham Soc., London, 1883

DONALDSON, H. H., AND DAVIS, D. J. A description of charts showing the areas of the cross sections of the human spinal cord at the level of each spinal nerve, *J. Comp. Neurol.* (Granville, O.), 13:19–40, 1903

FLUEGEL, F. E. Quelques recherches anatomiques sur la dégénérescence sénile de la moelle épinière, *Rev. Neurol.,* 1:618–623, May 1927

GELLERSTEDT, N. Zur Kenntnis der Hirnveränderungen bei der normalen Altersinvolution, *Upsala läkaref. förh.,* 38:193–408, 1933

GOWERS, W. R. *Diagnosis of Diseases of the Spinal Cord,* 2d ed. Blakiston, Philadelphia, 1881

NONNE, M. Rückenmarksuntersuchungen in Fällen von perniciöser Anämie, von Sepsis und von Senium, nebst Bemerkungen über Marchi-Veränderungen bei acut verlaufenden Rückenmarksprocessen, *Dtsch. Ztschr. Nervenh.* (Leipzig), 14:192–241, 1899

ONUF, B., AND COLLINS, J. Experimental researches on the localization of the sympathetic nerve in the spinal cord and brain, and contributions to its physiology, *J. Nerv. Ment. Dis.,* 25:661–678, Sept. 1898

SANDER, M. Untersuchungen über die Altersveränderungen im Rückenmark, *Dtsch. Ztschr. Nervenh.* (Leipzig), 17:369–396, 1900

STEBLOW, E. M., AND LOVCKAJA, A. J.   Ueber die primären pathologisch-anatomischen Veränderungen bei Tabes dorsalis; Sekundärer Charakter der tabetischen Entartung der Hinterstränge, *Ztschr. ges. Neurol. Psychiat.*, 155:729–742, 1936

STERN, K.   Beitrag zur Histopathologie des senilen Rückenmarks, *Ztschr. ges. Neurol. Psychiat.*, 155:543–554, 1936

TARLOV, I. M.   Structure of the nerve root; I—Nature of the junction between the central and the peripheral nervous system, *Arch. Neurol. Psychiat.*, 37:555–583, March 1937

———— Structure of the nerve root; II—Differentiation of sensory from motor roots; observations on identification of function in roots of mixed cranial nerves, *Arch. Neurol. Psychiat.*, 37:1338–1355, June 1937

WARTHIN, A. S.   *Old Age; the Major Involution; the Physiology and Pathology of the Aging Process.*   Hoeber, New York, 1929

WILLIAMSON, R. T.   *On the Relation of Diseases of the Spinal Cord to the Distribution and Lesions of the Spinal Blood Vessels.*   H. K. Lewis, London, 1895

———— *Diseases of the Spinal Cord.*   Oxford Univ. Press, London, 1908

WOLTMAN, H. W.   Arteriosclerosis of the nervous system; an analysis of 59 cases with cord changes, *M. Clin. N. Amer.*, 5:511–520, Sept. 1921

56

Part 2

Atlas

Atlas of a Normal Spinal Cord

In order to give a basis for comparison with pathological cords and cords of different ages, photographs and a description of each segment of a normal cord are presented on pages 64–124. The term "normal" is relative. The spinal cord used in this study was essentially free from morbid defects. It was removed shortly after death from the body of a twenty-four-year-old woman who died from subacute bacterial endocarditis. While an occasional focus of acute microglial proliferation was encountered in the cord, none of the foci happened to be located in a spot that would disturb the cell count. In one instance, a focus impinged on Clarke's column at the thoracic level, but this infiltration was so thin that Clarke's column cells could be clearly seen through it and the reaction was so recent that no phagocytosis had yet occurred. Otherwise the cord was free from defects.

After the sections were prepared in the manner described on page 5, photographs were made of the appropriate levels of both Weigert and Nissl preparations. The photographs of the Weigert sections were taken at 12 diameters magnification and of the Nissl preparations at 20 diameters magnification.* The cell pictures were printed on mat-surfaced paper that was suitable for drawing with China ink. On the right-hand side of each section the various cell columns were outlined in ink. Then the entire left-hand side of the section, together with the outlined cell columns on the right, were projected upon a photographic wash made from potassium ferricyanide and hyposulphite. All the unprojected parts of the photograph were washed away leaving isolated cell columns on the right to contrast with the corresponding columns on the left, the latter columns being shown in their natural background. The illustrations were then mounted in pairs with the myelin picture and the corresponding cell picture of each segment on a page. A brief description of the characteristics of each segment, together with the cell count, appears on the page facing each plate.

---

*All Weigert stains have been reproduced without reduction. Photographs of the Nissl stains have been reduced by 25 per cent, except for the first thoracic segment which has been reduced by 33⅓ per cent.

NOTE. The references cited in Part II are included in the list appended to Part I (pp. 53–56).

Cell Columns and Cell Counts

A great deal has been written on cell groupings and on segmental arrangements of cells in the human as well as in animal spinal cords. The well-known *Atlas* of Bruce[1] has until recently been perhaps the best exposition of the topography of the human cord. Bruce examined serial sections cut transversely, and by selecting every tenth section for study he arrived at his pattern of lateral and longitudinal cell arrangement. He was influenced considerably by the idea of cell grouping according to segmental levels and used this mode of division as the basis for his work; at only one or two levels did he break down the segmental arrangement into subdivisions. After selecting a Weigert section which he considered typical of any given segment, he described the characteristics of this section and then in a similar cell-stained section he counted the cells in the anterior horn and the intermediolateral columns and in Clarke's column when they were present. His descriptions of the myelin-stained sections were quite adequate and have been a great help to all workers in this field for the past forty years. His cell counts, however, have left something to be desired. In the first place, he considered the cells on only one side of the cord—omitting similar counts at the same level on the opposite side. Secondly, it is obvious to anyone who has had experience in the study of cell groups that two sections separated from each other by the thickness of ten or even five sections may show considerable difference in cell count. But more important than this is the difficulty of identifying cell columns that run longitudinally from a study of transversely cut sections. One's conception of the third dimension is rather strained when attempting to fit cell groups from another spinal cord into the level-by-level topographical pattern so explicitly laid down by Bruce.

In spite of the difficulties presented by the shortcomings of Bruce's *Atlas,* the work of other men appears even more inadequate. Dejerine,[34] and others have worked on the entire length of the cord, but their schemes of topography are unnecessarily complex because of divisions and subdivisions of cell columns beyond a reasonable classification. Shorter contributions have been less helpful than those of Bruce and Dejerine because the authors worked only on small portions of the cord, principally from the lumbo-sacral levels. The chief difficulty with all these schemes of cell distribution lies in the fact that they were based so completely on segmental arrangement within the spinal cord. Now, aside from the thoracic cord, where a certain monotony of cytological distribution is encountered throughout a good part of its length, there is apt

60

to be much variation between corresponding segments of two cords at points where the posterior nerve roots of higher segments make their exit. If one is a trifle higher or lower than the other, the cell patterns may not agree. In order to discover a close agreement in the location of corresponding columns and nuclei, the blocks have to be cut at varying distances; and even so, a given cell column may be present to its greatest extent on one side but scarcely discernible on the other, although the transverse section has been cut as perpendicularly as possible to its long axis. Study of embryonic human cords, as shown by Streeter,[35] suggests the segmental grouping of motor cells. But the adult human spinal cord has very largely lost its segmental character, and in all probability its adult relationships become established early in life. In the adult ostrich, by contrast, segmental grouping is still discernible. Paired motor nuclei with constricted necks, sparse in cells, are found joining contiguous segments even in the adult bird.

Recently an interesting and illuminating study was made by Elliott,[36] in which longitudinal as well as transverse sections were utilized and the projected images of individual cells in serial sections were superimposed one on the other in such a manner that the aggregate group gave a precise pattern of each cell column. His arrangement shows that the human spinal cord has indeed lost its segmental characteristics, and it now becomes possible for the first time to understand the confusing subdivisions encountered in the transverse sections.

Figure 24 and Figure 25 (taken from Elliott) illustrate in a diagrammatic way the arrangement of cell columns as seen in longitudinal section. The absence of any pattern that is based on segmental grouping is clearly seen. In all probability, groups of cells that receive similar stimuli from higher centers, and that function together as bases of similar motor units, migrate from one segment to another in the direction whence their stimuli arise, thus forming the cell columns shown in Figures 24 and 25. This would accord with the well-known neurobiotactic law of Ariens Kappers. The inadequacy of the old idea of segmental grouping has always been felt clinically, and the confusion concerning the segmental innervation of muscles will perhaps now be more understandable.

With Elliott's scheme as a frame of reference, we therefore made an attempt to determine the number of motor cells in the anterior horn and the number of cells in Clarke's column as well as in the intermediolateral column at some part of each spinal segment. Even though the variation from the rostral to the caudal end of each segment is great, reference to Figure 25 makes it possible to locate the plane of any section and so compare it with similar sections from other cords. This aids one in making reliable cell counts and decreases the difficulty of learning whether an actual loss in the number of cells has taken place. There still remains the question of anterior horn gliosis in old age, which is difficult to interpret, as well as the question of open nests, where apparently the nerve cells of the cord formerly lay (see pp. 30 and 46).

61

The problem of just what to count always presents itself. Any fragment of pericaryon that contains Nissl bodies might be considered part of the legitimate count, but frequently two or more bases of dendrites from the cell might be transected by the plane of section and when counted give an erroneous number. To circumvent this difficulty one might count either nuclei or nucleoli rather than fragments of cell bodies, but here another difficulty is encountered owing to the large size of the anterior horn cells, which sometimes reaches 120 micra in their rostro-caudal diameter. If the number of nuclei, or more especially the number of nucleoli, were taken as a criterion of the number of cells present at any given level, it might frequently be recorded that virtually no cells were present. Sometimes the number of nuclei and particularly of nucleoli showing in a thin section is almost zero even when the microscopic field is fairly well filled with nerve cell bodies. This difficulty was corrected by counting nuclei in contiguous sections in a cube measuring .25 mm. in each direction (250 micra), which is twice the rostro-caudal length of an anterior horn cell. Since the cell is three times as long as it is wide[37] and the nucleus occupies only two-thirds or less of the transverse diameter, the probability of transecting the nucleus more than once in sections 24 micra thick is not great. The number of nuclei in a block 240 micra thick would therefore represent the number of cells in such a block with a fair degree of accuracy. This procedure has been successfully followed in the brain by Conel[38] in his study of the development of the cerebral cortex. It must be admitted that such a method of counting is rarely of value to a practical neuropathologist, for ten consecutive sections would seldom be available to him for study. As a rule, he must decide from an examination of one or two sections whether there is a loss of nerve cells. Of course, this is usually apparent from the pathological reaction, when such a reaction is present, but there is apt to be little of a pathological nature in a senescent spinal cord upon which to base a deduction.

While knowing the number of nuclei in a .25 mm. block may not be of pragmatic value to a busy pathologist, it seems particularly well suited to the problem of determining the loss of nerve cells in advancing age. By comparing a series of transverse sections with Elliott's longitudinal charts, one can fit the block he is studying almost exactly into its appropriate level of the segment. This does not mean, however, that all the difficulties are thereby resolved, for it frequently happens that the cell columns are not bilaterally symmetrical, even though the block was transected as perpendicularly as possible to its long axis. That is, the nodes of condensation of nerve cells do not always occur at precisely the same level, so that in the very same .25 mm. block the total count of one column may be higher on the right side than on the left, while the total count of another column may be higher on the left side than on the right. As a consequence, one must be cautious in comparing the right side of the cord with the left side. For this reason, especially, it was thought that counts made on single sections would be of limited value.

62

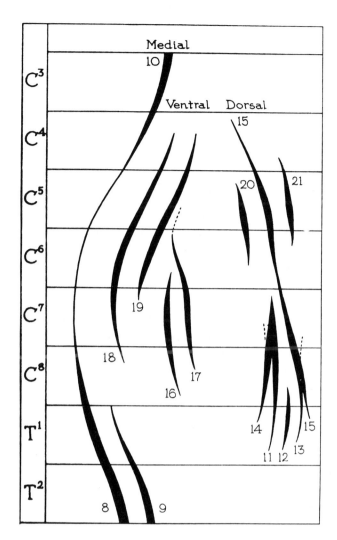

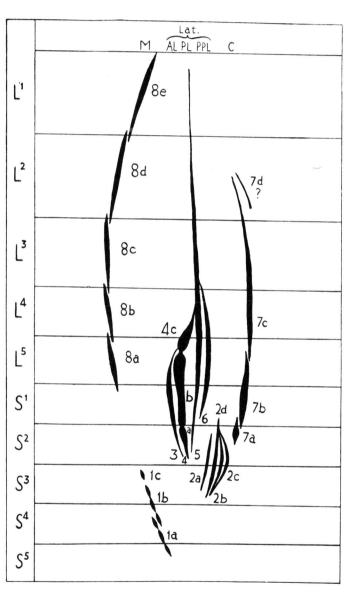

*Reproduced by kind permission of
The Wister Institute from the originals
of Figures 4 and 6 in an article by
Harry C. Elliott, Am. J. Anat., 70:95–117*

*Figure 25
Diagram showing the
arrangement of cell columns*

First Cervical Segment

Observations from Weigert Preparation

The outline of the transverse section of the cord at this level is roughly ellipsoidal, with the short axis running vertically. Four notches appear on the convexity: two on the ventral side at Helveg's triangle and two on the dorsal side at the entrance of each posterior root. The anterior horns are broader than they are at the next lower level, and their outer boundaries are continuous with well-formed lateral horns. Posterior to the lateral horns the gray matter undergoes a distinct constriction and then flares out laterodorsally in paddle-shaped posterior horns, each with a broad, conspicuous substantia gelatinosa Rolandi. Lateral to the constricted waist of the gray matter the formatio reticularis occupies about one-third of the width of the funiculus lateralis.

Observations from Preparation Stained for Nerve Cells

There are only a few cells in the anterior horn at this level, and they are chiefly comprised in two groups. The first (subdivided by Bruce into anterior and posterior mesial groups and called column 10 by Elliott) is situated in the tip of the horn. The second group, situated slightly dorsolateral to the first group, belongs to the nucleus of the spinal accessory nerve. A cluster of cells of the intermediolateral column may be seen in the lateral horn, and the small granular cells of the substantia gelatinosa Rolandi, as well as the larger cells of the basal and pericornual groups, in the posterior horn.

Nuclear counts at this level were not recorded.

64

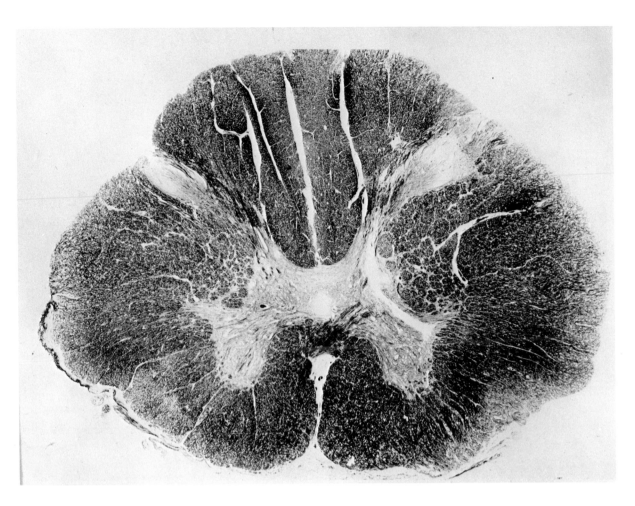

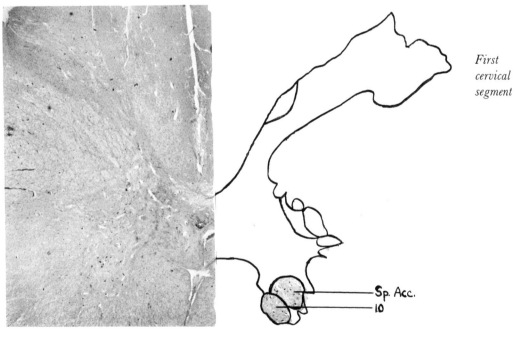

*First
cervical
segment*

Sp. Acc.

10

65

Second Cervical Segment

Weigert Preparation

The outline of the transverse section of the cord at this level approaches that of a circle. The anterior horns are narrower than in C 1 but the lateral horns are still conspicuous. Helweg's triangle is seen as a pale area on the ventrolateral borders of the section. The posterior horns are long and slim and curve only slightly toward the dorsolateral borders. The formatio reticularis is reduced in size; the substantia gelatinosa is much scantier; and the gray matter as a whole is much bulkier.

Nerve Cells

The anterior horn cells may be divided into two groups: the medial group and the spinal accessory group (see under C 1). In the lateral horn there are the very small cells of the intermediolateral column, and in the posterior horn the small cells of the substantia gelatinosa as well as the larger cells of the apical, basal, and pericornual groups.

The nuclear counts in a .25 mm. block were as follows:

Group	Left	Right
Medial	66	55
Spinal accessory	67	64
Intermediolateral column	131	124

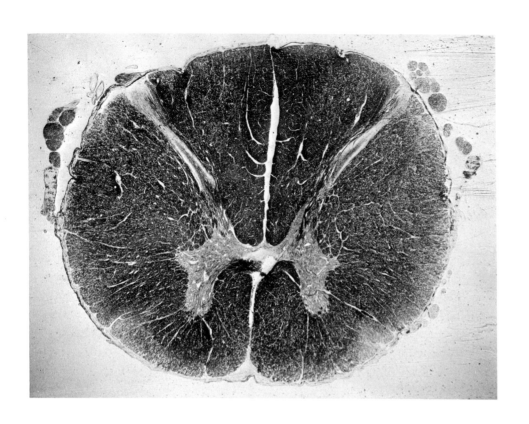

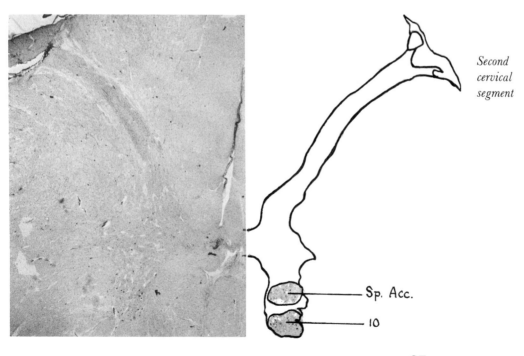

Second cervical segment

Sp. Acc.

10

67

Third Cervical Segment

Weigert Preparation

The cord is approximately circular in outline at this level. The only interruptions in the contour of the section occur at Helveg's triangle (near the ventrolateral border) and in the posterior root zone. The anterior horns are long and slim, with nearly parallel sides. The lateral horns are smaller and blunter than in C 2. The formatio reticularis is further reduced in size. The posterior horns are even slimmer than in C 2, and the substantia gelatinosa suggests a tenpin in shape. As the gray matter is considerably reduced in bulk, the white matter is conspicuous; the large triangular masses of the posterior funiculi are particularly prominent.

Nerve Cells

Again, the cells in the anterior horn may be divided into the medial and the spinal accessory group. As in C 2, there is a group of small cells in the lateral horn, and the small cells of the substantia gelatinosa as well as the customary occasional cells of the apical, basal, and pericornual groups may be seen in the posterior horn.

The nuclear counts in a .25 mm. block were as follows:

Group	Left	Right
Medial	28	35
Spinal accessory	30	42
Intermediolateral column	—	—

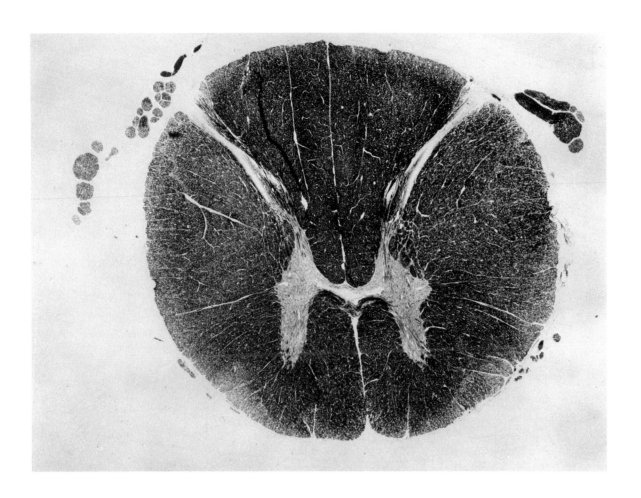

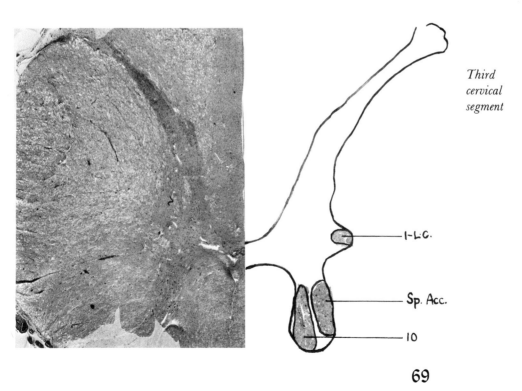

*Third
cervical
segment*

1-L.C.

Sp. Acc.

10

69

Fourth Cervical Segment

Weigert Preparation

The outline of the cord at this level tends to be ellipsoidal, with the short axis running vertically. Helveg's triangle is less distinct than in C 3. The anterior horns have begun to extend laterally, so that their borders are nearly equal in length. The formatio reticularis is further reduced in size and situated somewhat more dorsally. The diameter of the posterior horns is further diminished, and the substantia gelatinosa is retracted from the periphery by a bottle-necked constriction in the horn. However, the apex of the posterior funiculus is broader than it was in sections obtained from more rostral segments.

Nerve Cells

The cells of the anterior horn are divisible into two main groups, the medial (Elliott's column 10) and the lateral. The lateral may be further subdivided into anterolateral (column 18) and posterolateral (column 15). In addition, there are a few small granular cells scattered through the gelatinous substance and a few cells of the basal, apical, and pericornual groups.

The nuclear counts in a .25 mm. block were as follows:

Group	Column	Left	Right
Medial	10	58	49
Anterolateral	18	19	—
Posterolateral	15	15	21

70

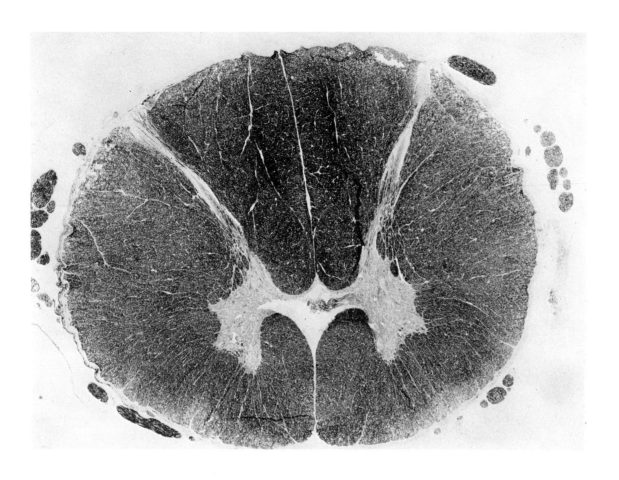

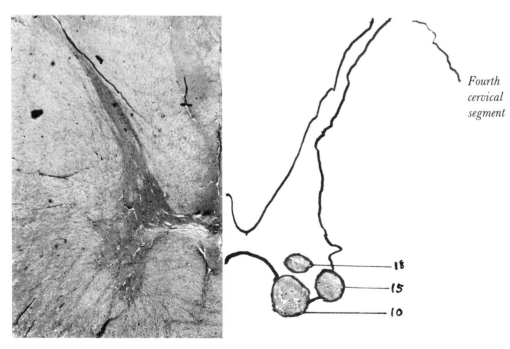

*Fourth
cervical
segment*

18

15

10

Fifth Cervical Segment

Weigert Preparation

This section is ellipsoidal in outline, with the short axis extending vertically. Helweg's triangle has disappeared, and the only interruptions of contour are made by notches where nerve roots were present. The gray matter is considerably more voluminous than in C 4. The anterior horns assume roughly the form of a pentagon, with the base posterior and the apex anterior. The shape of the posterior horns suggests a bottle, with the base centrally and the neck peripherally placed. The formatio reticularis is further diminished and is here as conspicuous in the gray as in the white matter. The anterior and posterior commissures are of about the same width.

Nerve Cells

The large anterior horn cells may be divided into the medial group, which is now called column 8, the anterolateral groups (columns 18 and 19), and the posterolateral groups (columns 15 and 20). In addition there are the customary cells in the posterior horn.

The nuclear counts in a .25 mm. block were as follows:

Group	Column	Left	Right
Medial	8	43	35
Anterolateral	18	25	33
	19	14	8
Posterolateral	15	64	49
	20	11	11

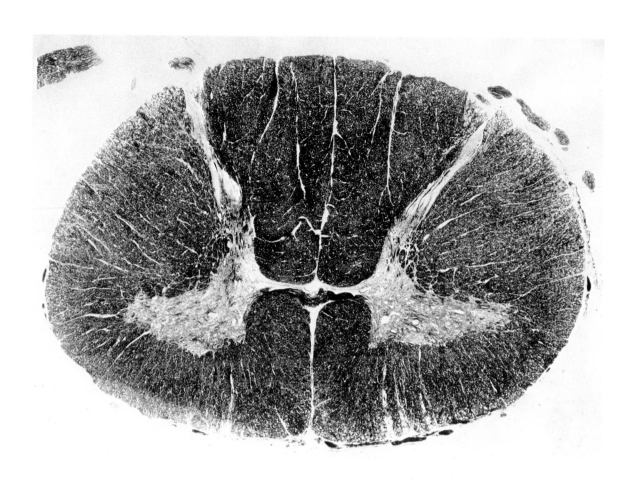

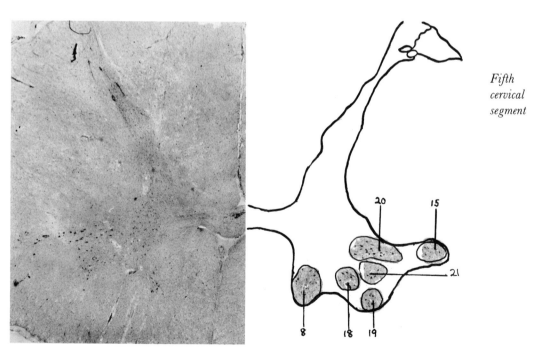

*Fifth
cervical
segment*

73

Sixth Cervical Segment

Weigert Preparation

The lateral projection of the anterior horn continues to increase in bulk, and its posterior border tends to become concave as the cell columns increase in number. The posterior horn is more voluminous than in C 5, but the formatio reticularis is still of about the same size as in the segment above.

Nerve Cells

The medial cell group is distinctly separated from the lateral groups and is considered to be one column rather than to be divisible into anterior and posteriormesial groups as described by Bruce. The lateral projection contains the fine subdivisions so clearly shown by Elliott. Columns 15, 20, and 21 might be termed posterolateral nuclei and 17 and 19 anterolateral nuclei, but at this level 18 defies classification with either. In the posterior horn the small cells of the gelatinous substance and the larger cells of the sensory pathways appear in the customary manner.

The nuclear counts in a .25 mm. block were as follows:

Group	Column	Left	Right
Medial	8	39	47
	18	39	38
Anterolateral	19	33	27
	17	50	26
Posterolateral	21	24	26
	15	63	53
	20	34	32

74

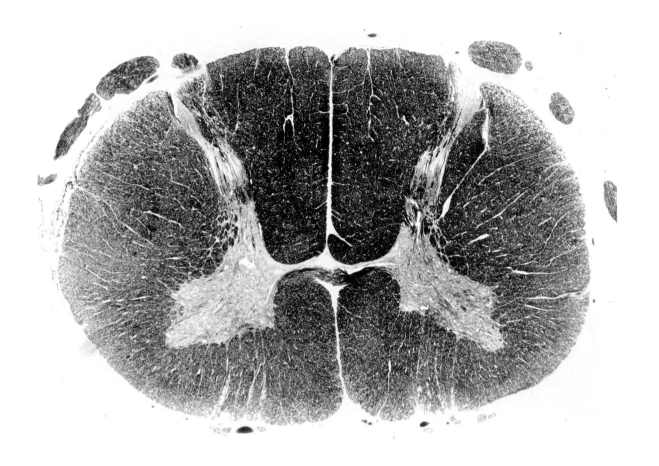

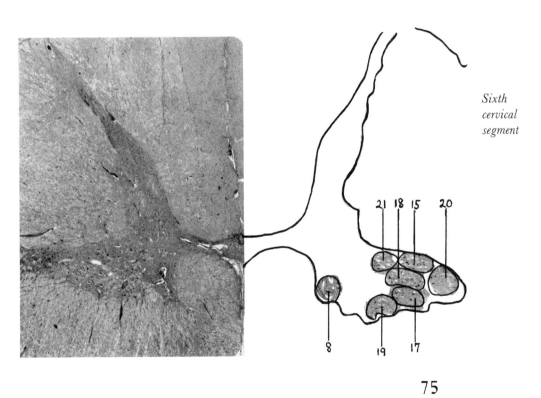

Sixth
cervical
segment

21 18 15   20

8   19   17

Seventh Cervical Segment

Weigert Preparation

The lateral projection of the anterior horn has become so blunted at this level that the cornu is practically quadrilateral. The anterior border is longer than the posterior because of its undulating course. The formatio reticularis is still present.

Nerve Cells

The lateral cell groups lie mostly in the anterior portion of the cornu, which fact helped produce the undulating border seen in the Weigert. The posterior border is shorter, since only one cell column lies in that region.

The nuclear counts in a .25 mm. block were as follows:

Group	Column	Left	Right
Medial	8	16	18
Anterolateral	17	16	26
	18	59	45
	16	37	60
Posterolateral	15	48	43

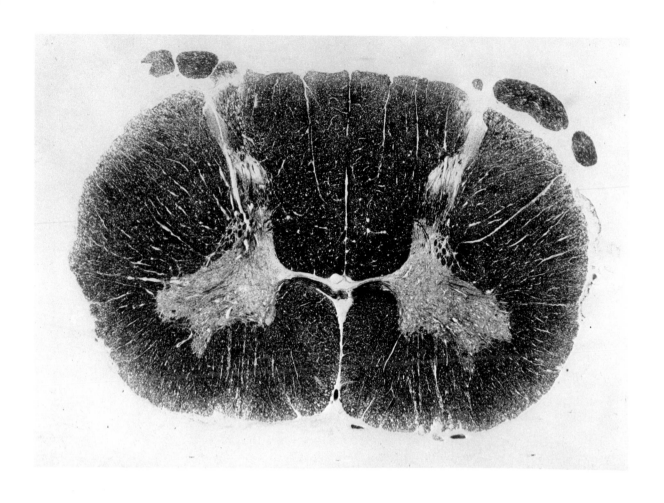

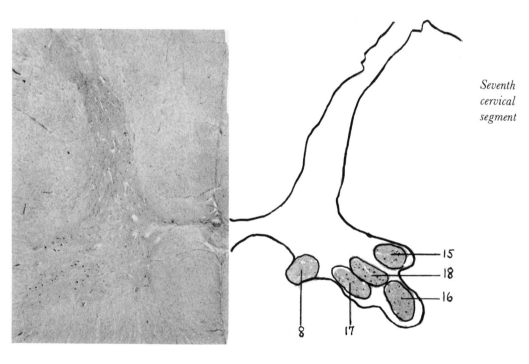

15

18

16

8

17

Eighth Cervical Segment

Upper Part

Weigert Preparation

The absence of segmental characteristics is clearly illustrated by the appearance of this section and the one shown on page 81, both of which were taken from a block between the seventh cervical and the first thoracic nerve roots. In this section the anterior border of the anterior horn presents two concavities separated by a sharp projection of gray matter. The lateral projection is more sharply pointed than in C 7 and T1. The posterior horn is slim and long, and the posterior columns are very deep.

Nerve Cells

Column 8 is the only one that is distinctly medial, although columns 17 and 18 are pushed far in toward the midline (possibly by the compression of white matter against the medial cusp of the ventral surface). Columns 17 and 18 are illustrated in the figure, but the separation may be slightly artificial when judged only by transverse sections. The cells were so close together that the nuclear counts of those two columns were considered as one.

The nuclear counts in a .25 mm. block were as follows:

Group	Column	Left	Right
Medial	8	19	22
Anterolateral	17, 18	21	20
Posterolateral	11	32	40
	13	33	47
	14	56	45
	15	56	75

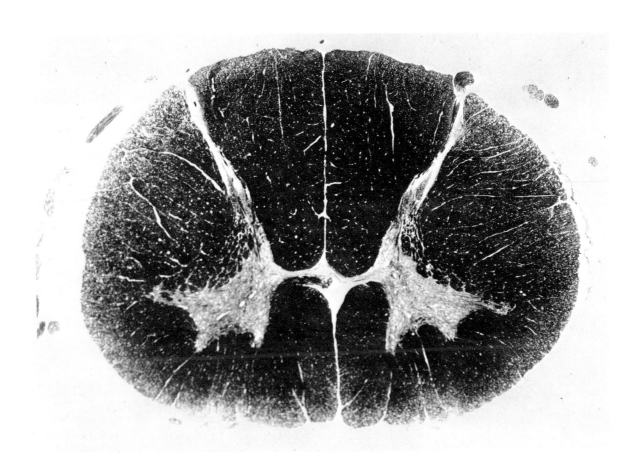

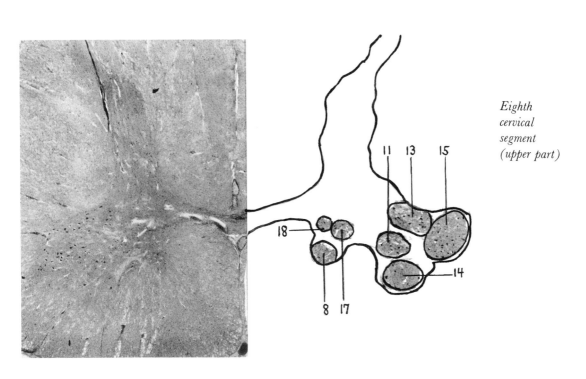

Eighth cervical segment (upper part)

Eighth Cervical Segment

Lower Part

Weigert Preparation

The outline of the cord at this level continues to be ellipsoidal, but the horizontal axis more closely approaches the vertical axis in length. Aside from the projection for column 8, the anterior horn is roughly rhomboidal. The formatio reticularis is meager in extent and better seen in the gray than in the white matter.

Nerve Cells

The blunt lateral projection of the anterior horn contains five distinct groups, which are separated by a wide interval from that of the medially situated column 8. All these cells belong to the posterolateral groups, the anterolateral groups having disappeared at this level. The larger cells of the basal, apical, and pericornual groups appear more numerous; the small granular cells of the posterior horn deserve no special comment.

The nuclear counts in a .25 mm. block were as follows:

Group	Column	Left	Right
Medial	8	41	47
Posterolateral	11	32	27
	12	15	17
	13	27	28
	14	15	13
	15	36	33

80

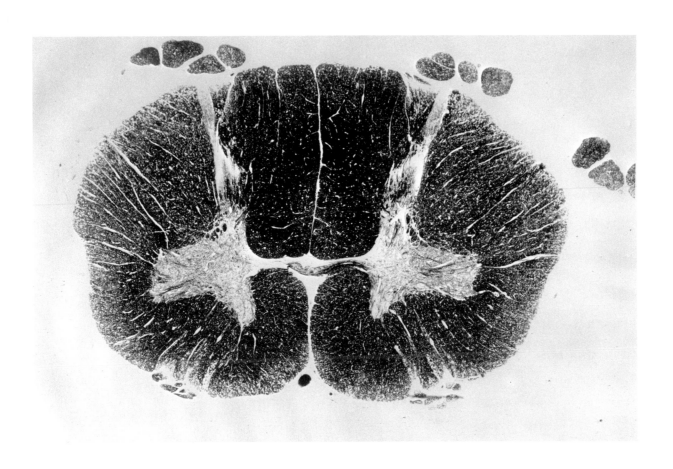

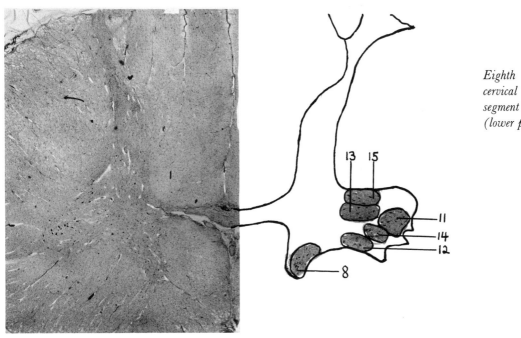

*Eighth
cervical
segment
(lower part)*

13 15

11

14
12

8

81

First Thoracic Segment

Weigert Preparation

The outline of the transverse section of the cord at this level is somewhat flattened on its dorsal surface, and the vertical axis is still distinctly shorter than the horizontal. The good-sized lateral projections of the anterior horns are beginning to develop points. The posterior horns have assumed the nearly parallel positions which give the gray matter of the thoracic segments its typical H-shaped configuration.

Nerve Cells

Column 8 is conspicuous, and column 9 is probably just beginning to appear. The intermediolateral column is large and drawn out in its lateral diameter. A small remnant of the tail of column 12 seems to be still present. In the region just lateral and dorsal to the posterior gray commissure there are a few large nerve cells on each side which constitute the beginning of the dorsal nucleus (Clarke's column).

Nuclear counts at this level were not recorded.

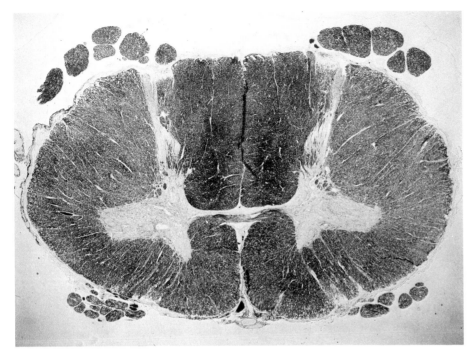

*First
thoracic
segment*

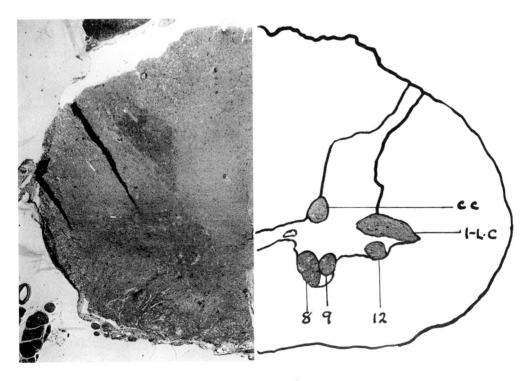

c c

1-L·C

8 9

12

83

Second Thoracic Segment

Weigert Preparation

While the outline of the cord tends toward the circular, the vertical axis is still the shorter. The bulky lateral projections of the anterior cornua are reduced to stubby, pointed horns. The posterior horns are nearly parallel to each other on their medial aspects.

Nerve Cells

The cells of the anterior horn are now divisible into two groups, one slightly lateral to the other. Elliott calls these groups columns 8 and 9, but the cells are sometimes so closely intermingled that they appear to belong to a single column. The small cells of the vegetative system and the intermediolateral column cells are also seen in this section, as well as the cells of Clarke's column, which are easily distinguishable on the medial aspect of the base of the posterior horn.

The nuclear counts in a .25 mm. block were as follows:

Group	Column	Left	Right
Medial	8	37	28
	9	18	42
	Intermediolateral	96	181
	Clarke's	23	30

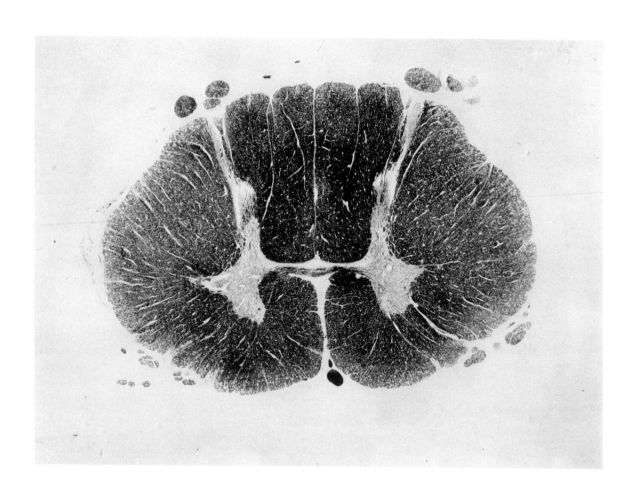

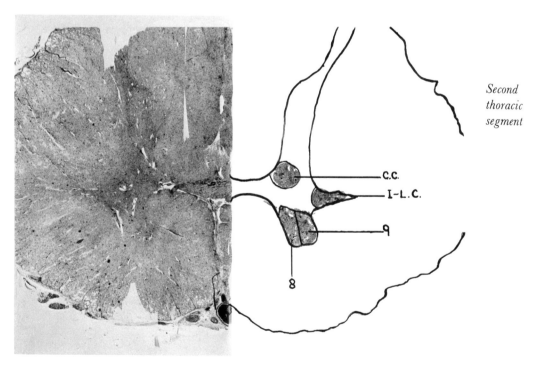

*Second
thoracic
segment*

C.C.

I-L.C.

9

8

Third Thoracic Segment

Weigert Preparation

The anterior horns are shorter and flatter than in more rostral segments, and a slight concavity on the left side of the ventral surface suggests a division between columns 8 and 9. At this level the lateral projections are shorter than usual. The medial edges of the central portions of the posterior horns are still roughly parallel.

Nerve Cells

The anterior horn cells are the same as in the segment immediately above, and the same small granular cells are scattered throughout the central portion of the posterior horn. These are flanked as usual by the basal, apical, and pericornual groups.

The nuclear counts in a .25 mm. block were as follows:

Group	Column	Left	Right
Medial	8	20	39
	9	24	40
	Intermediolateral	224	172
	Clarke's	22	20

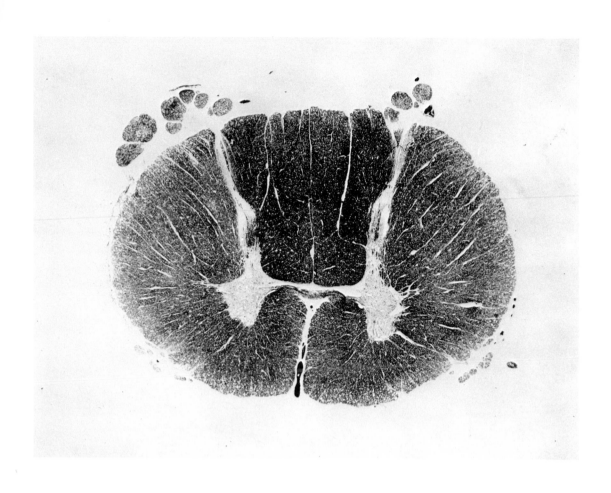

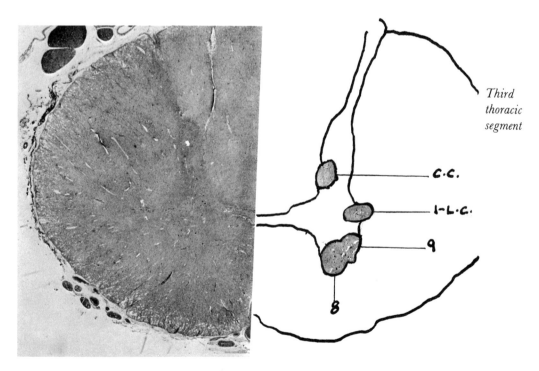

*Third
thoracic
segment*

C.C.

I-L.C.

9

8

87

Fourth Thoracic Segment

Weigert Preparation

The anterior horns are not so flattened as in T 3, and the lateral projections are more distinctly formed at this level of the cord than they are at the level shown in T 3. The slightly dorsolateral flare of the posterior horns gives a shape suggesting a trapezoid to the posterior funiculi.

Nerve Cells

The nuclear counts in a .25 mm. block were as follows:

Group	Column	Left	Right
Medial	8	26	24
	9	17	24
	Intermediolateral	251	176
	Clarke's	18	37

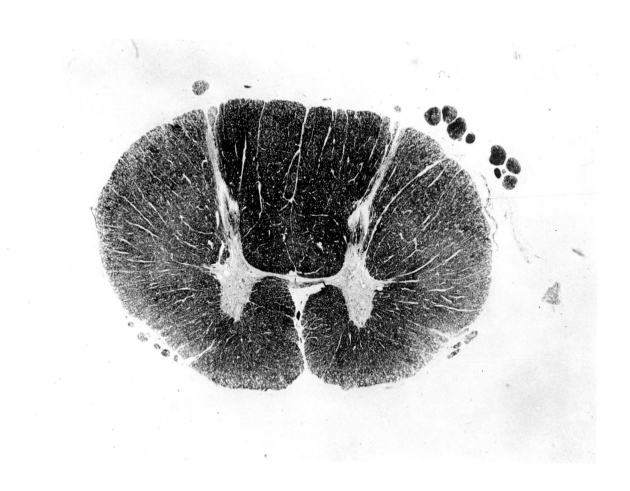

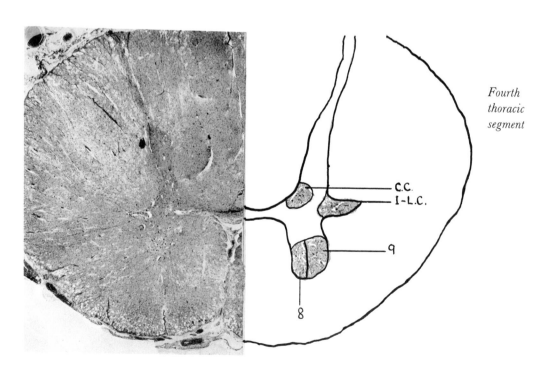

C.C.

I–L.C.

q

8

*Fourth
thoracic
segment*

Fifth Thoracic Segment

Weigert Preparation

The anterior horns are narrower and more delicate in appearance than in T 4, especially on the right. The lateral horns are well formed and sharply pointed. The lateral edges of the posterior funiculi slant dorsolaterally all the way from the posterior commissure to the periphery.

Nerve Cells

The nuclear counts in a .25 mm. block were as follows:

Group	Column	Left	Right
Medial	8	23	9
	9	24	18
	Intermediolateral	157	124
	Clarke's	26	40

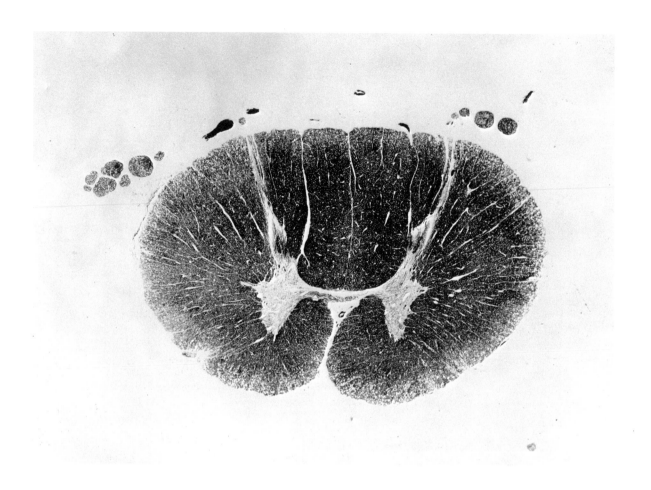

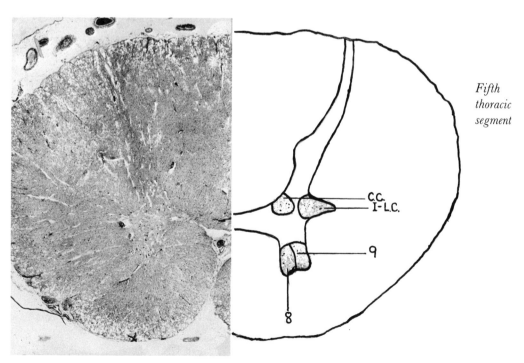

*Fifth
thoracic
segment*

C.C.
I-L.C.

9

8

91

Sixth Thoracic Segment

Weigert Preparation

There is no appreciable alteration in the shape of the anterior horns, but the lateral horns are slightly more blunted than in T 5. The obliquity of the posterior horns continues, giving the posterior funiculi increasingly broader bases.

Nerve Cells

Columns 8 and 9 are practically indistinguishable from each other, situated as they are in the pointed anterior cornu, so that while the following figures are accurate for the entire medial group, they are rather arbitrarily divided between the two columns.

The nuclear counts in a .25 mm. block were as follows:

Group	Column	Left	Right
Medial	8	29	19
	9	12	16
	Intermediolateral	80	162
	Clarke's	34	56

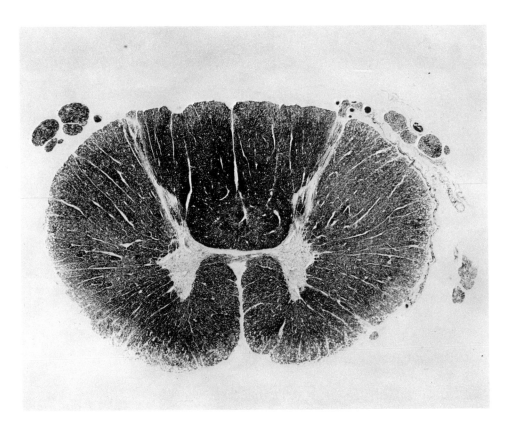

Sixth
thoracic
segment

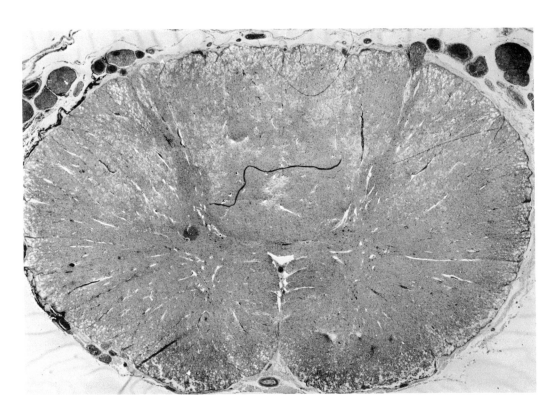

Seventh Thoracic Segment

Weigert Preparation

The outline of the cord continues to be ellipsoidal, and the anterior horns are narrower. The lateral horns extend only slightly into the lateral funiculi. The posterior horns continue to slant gracefully to the dorso-lateral periphery, as the lateral funiculi diminish in size. The posterior funiculus appears relatively larger.

Nerve Cells

The nuclear counts in a .25 mm. block were as follows:

Group	Column	Left	Right
Medial	8	19	18
	9	12	24
	Intermediolateral	67	93
	Clarke's	55	45

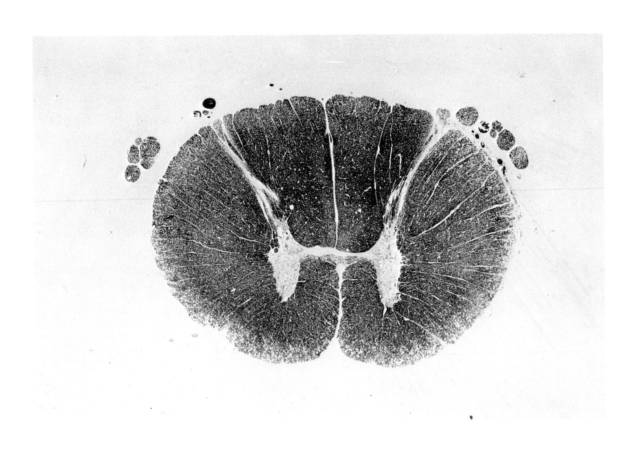

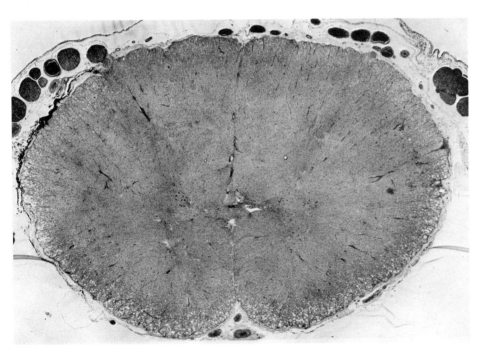

*Seventh
thoracic
segment*

95

Eighth Thoracic Segment

Weigert Preparation

The anterior horns present no marked difference from the foregoing segment. The dorsolateral course of the posterior horns gives an increased width to the base of the posterior funiculi; and the horns are greatly constricted from the gelatinous substance to the periphery.

Nerve Cells

The nuclear counts in a .25 mm. block were as follows:

Group	Column	Left	Right
Medial	8	24	8
	9	10	13
	Intermediolateral	161	75
	Clarke's	34	65

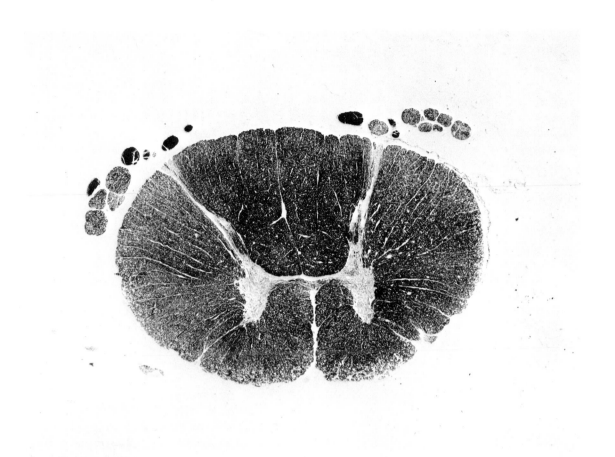

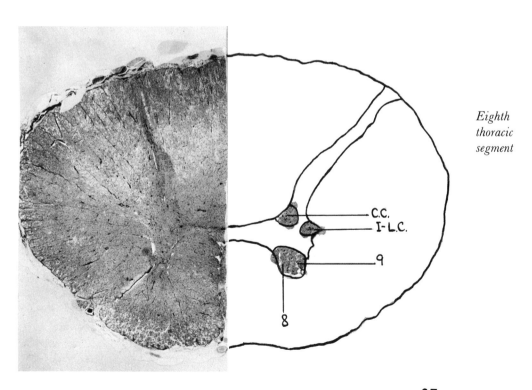

C.C.

I-L.C.

9

8

Eighth thoracic segment

97

Ninth Thoracic Segment

Weigert Preparation

The anterior horns slope ventrolaterally on their medial surface. The anterior surface is rounded off, while the lateral surface extends almost vertically backward. The lateral projections have almost disappeared.

Nerve Cells

Column 9 is slightly more anterior than column 8. The cells of the intermediolateral column, instead of being collected in a lateral-horn projection, lie along the edge of the gray matter at the junction of the anterior and posterior horns.

The nuclear counts in a .25 mm. block were as follows:

Group	Column	Left	Right
Medial	8	28	20
	9	29	29
	Intermediolateral	95	89
	Clarke's	75	65

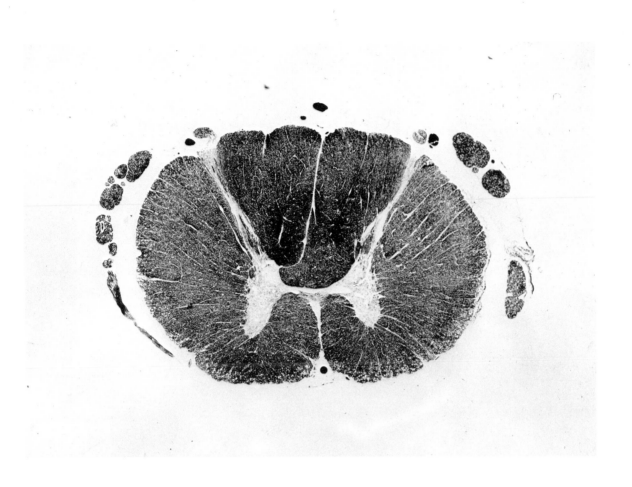

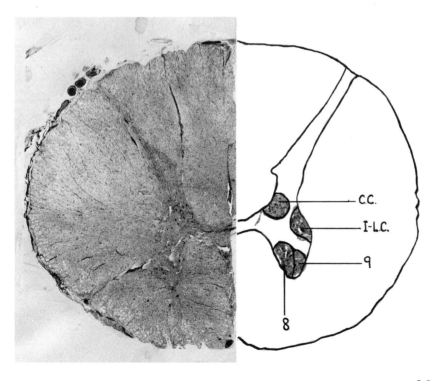

*Ninth
thoracic
segment*

C.C.

I-L.C.

9

8

99

Tenth Thoracic Segment

Weigert Preparation

The anterior horns continue to be roughly quadrangular, although there is a conspicuous lateral projection on the right side. It often happens, even though a block has been transected as perpendicularly as possible to its long axis, that the configuration of one side differs from the other. The posterior horns spread fanwise dorsolaterally, giving the appearance of a broad-based triangle to the posterior funiculi.

Nerve Cells

The nuclear counts in a .25 mm. block were as follows:

Group	Column	Left	Right
Medial	8	21	10
	9	19	24
	Intermediolateral	147	114
	Clarke's	31	64

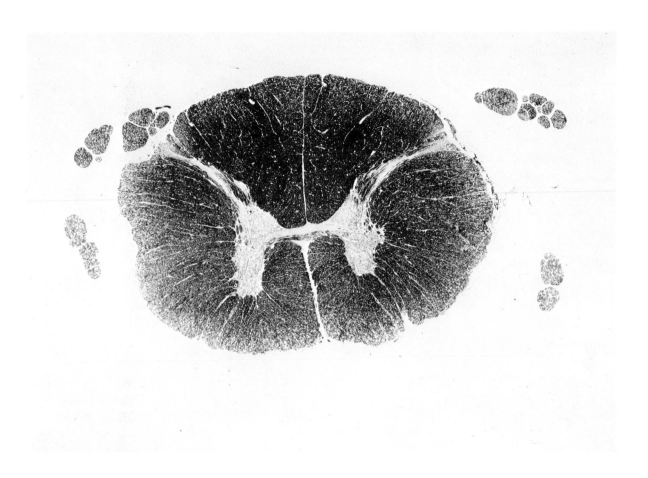

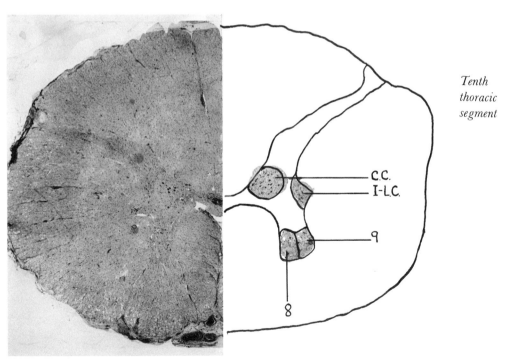

*Tenth
thoracic
segment*

C.C.

I-L.C.

9

8

101

Eleventh Thoracic Segment

Weigert Preparation

The anterior horns are more substantial in appearance, being noticeably broader, particularly at the base; the lateral horns, small but well formed, are situated at their posterolateral angles. The posterior horns are widely divergent, so that the obtuseness of the triangles of the posterior funiculus reaches its maximum degree.

Nerve Cells

The cells of column 8 are considerably smaller than those of column 9 and smaller than any cells in column 8 which have been encountered more rostrally. Most of the cells that contribute to the intermediolateral column lie along the ventrolateral border of the posterior horn rather than in the lateral horn itself.

The nuclear counts in a .25 mm. block were as follows:

Group	Column	Left	Right
Medial	8	40	25
	9	11	24
	Intermediolateral	195	172
	Clarke's	45	39

102

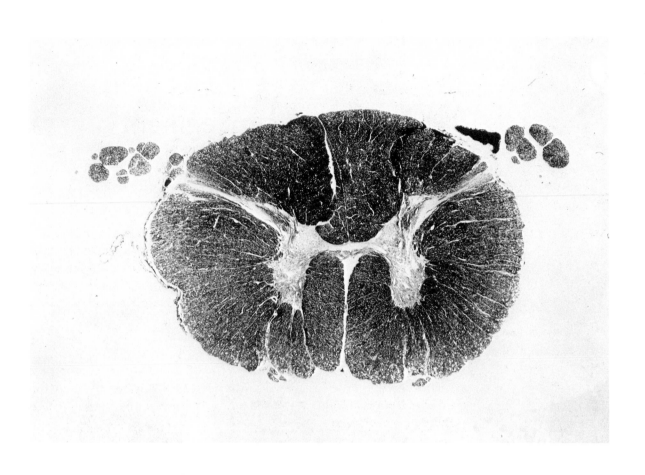

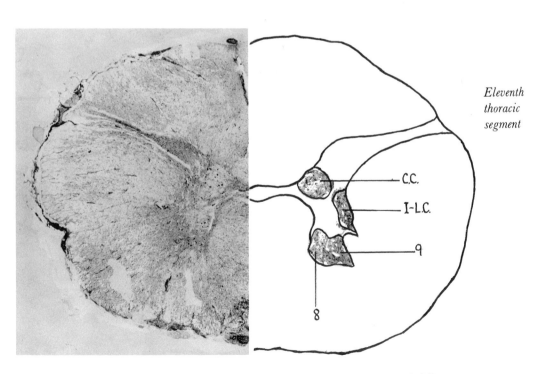

Eleventh thoracic segment

C.C.

I-L.C.

9

8

103

Twelfth Thoracic Segment

Weigert Preparation

The anterior horns continue to increase in volume, being considerably broader here than in the middle thoracic region. The lateral horns are well formed and bulk large at the posterolateral angle of the anterior horn. The posterior horns have also begun to increase in size, and the gelatinous substance is much broader than in more rostral thoracic segments.

Nerve Cells

As in all lower thoracic segments, columns 8 and 9 are scarcely distinguishable from each other. Consequently, the division in the cell count is more or less arbitrary.

The nuclear counts in a .25 mm. block were as follows:

Group	Column	Left	Right
Medial	8	20	21
	9	29	17
	Intermediolateral	256	208
	Clarke's	64	21

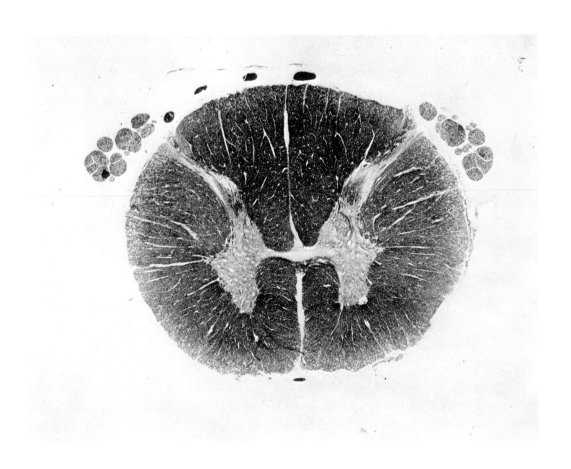

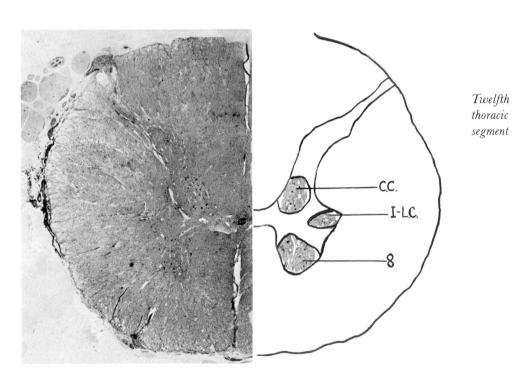

*Twelfth
thoracic
segment*

C.C.

I-L.C.

8

105

First Lumbar Segment

Weigert Preparation

The cord is now distinctly circular in outline, and the transition between the thoracic and lumbar levels is seen macroscopically to greatest advantage in the increased width of both the anterior and the posterior horns. The well-myelinated Clarke's column impinges medially onto the posterior funiculus, and the substantia gelatinosa continues to increase in volume.

Nerve Cells

Reference to Figure 25 (taken from Elliott) will show why some authors (following Bruce) have divided the medial group into anterior mesial and posterior mesial. Columns 4, 5, and 6 are lateral to column 8 but are indistinguishable from one another. The cells of the basal, apical, and pericornual groups are larger and more conspicuous than those seen in the more rostral segments.

The nuclear counts in a .25 mm. block were as follows:

Group	Column	Left	Right
Medial	8	29	35
Lateral	4, 5, 6	23	24
	Intermediolateral	141	179
	Clarke's	26	65

Stilling's nucleus, anterior to Clarke's column, was omitted from the cell count as it was in the cervical segments, because of the small size of many of its cells.

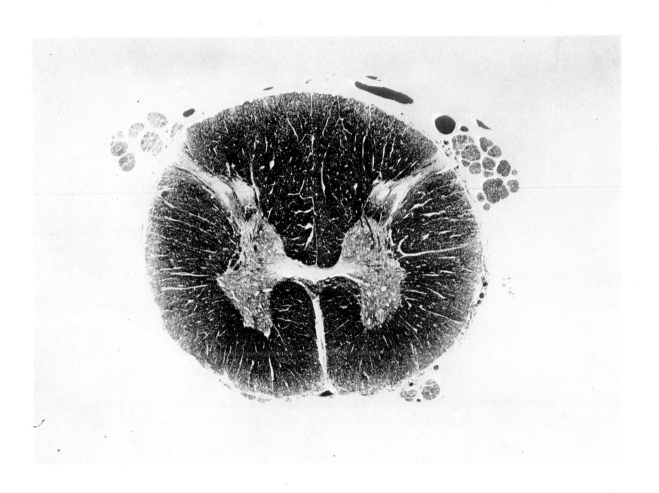

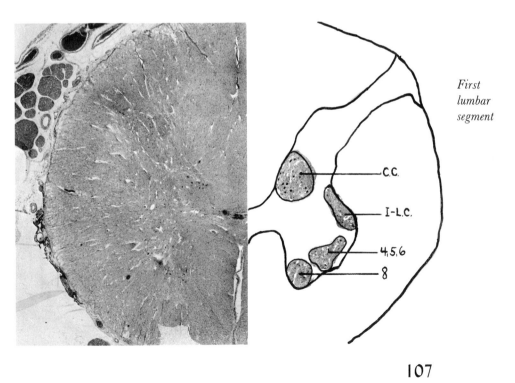

*First
lumbar
segment*

C.C.

I-L.C.

4,5,6

8

Second Lumbar Segment

Weigert Preparation

The anterior horns now present a squarish appearance because of the building up of their posterolateral regions by the advent of posterolateral column cells. The lateral-horn projection has disappeared, while Clarke's column is still present but small.

Nerve Cells

The cells of the medial group continue to make up column 8. While columns 4, 5, and 6 appear in the anterior part of the anterior horn at this level, they contribute to the posterolateral columns of more caudal segments. On the other hand, column 7, which is situated posteriorly at this level, swings toward the center in more caudal segments.

The nuclear counts in a .25 mm. block were as follows:

Group	Column	Left	Right
Medial	8	37	39
Lateral	4, 5, 6	61	41
Central	7	27	21
	Clarke's	29	21

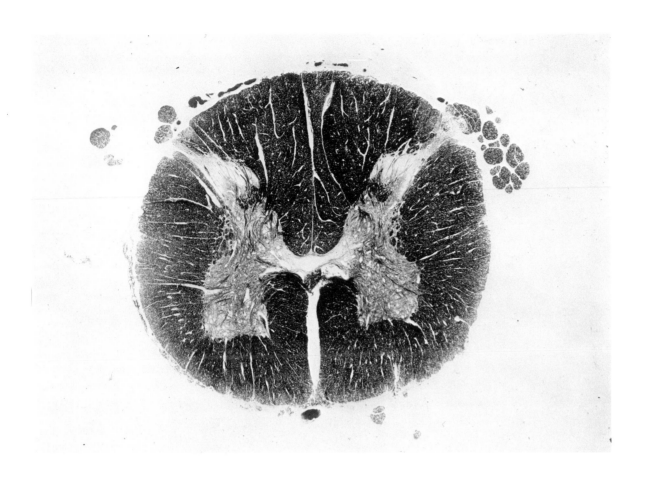

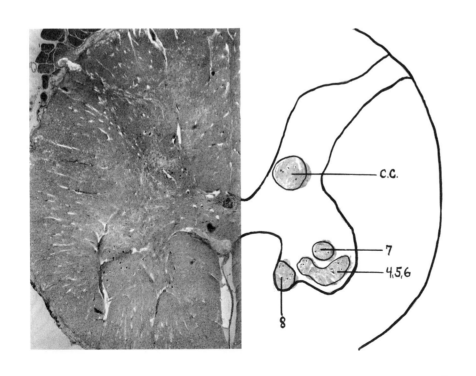

*Second
lumbar
segment*

c.c.

7

4,5,6

8

Third Lumbar Segment

Weigert Preparation

The large proportion of gray matter to white matter which is so characteristic of the lower cord is seen to good advantage at this level. The anterior and posterior horns are broad and bulky, while the lateral funiculi are shallow and long and the posterior funiculus is narrow and deep.

Nerve Cells

Clarke's column has now disappeared, and in the lateral projection of the anterior horn columns 4, 5, and 6 have shifted to an anteroposterior position near the lateral border. Column 7 consists of at least two parts (b and c) and has begun to shift toward the center.

The nuclear counts in a .25 mm. block were as follows:

Group	Column	Left	Right
Medial	8	67	51
Lateral	4, 5, 6	175	141
Central	7	102	81

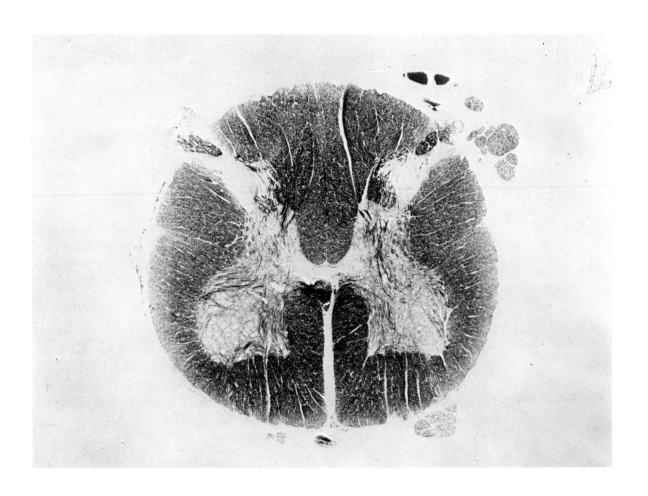

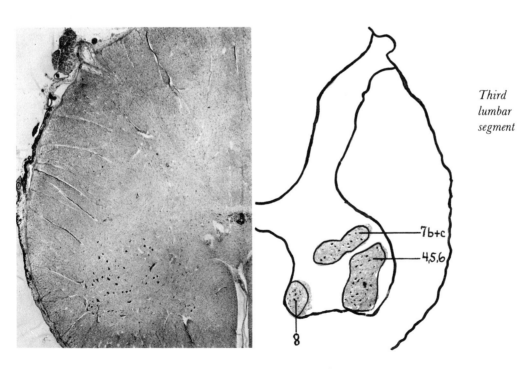

*Third
lumbar
segment*

7b+c

4,5,6

8

| | |

Fourth Lumbar Segment

Weigert Preparation

The anterior horns continue to expand laterodorsally. The beginning of a division between the antero- and posterolateral cell groups is indicated by a notch in the lateral surface of the horn. As the posterior horns have grown broader, the posterior commissure has increased in depth.

Nerve Cells

In the lateral projection of the anterior horn, columns 4, 5, and 6 can now be distinguished from one another. Column 7 has shifted to its most characteristic central location. On the anterior border of the anterior horn, directly ahead of column 7, lies a group of small cells which make up the anterior column.

The nuclear counts in a .25 mm. block were as follows:

Group	Column	Left	Right
Medial	8	40	48
Anterior	—	41	28
Central	7	74	97
Anterolateral	4	36	46
Posterolateral	5	58	78
	6	35	64

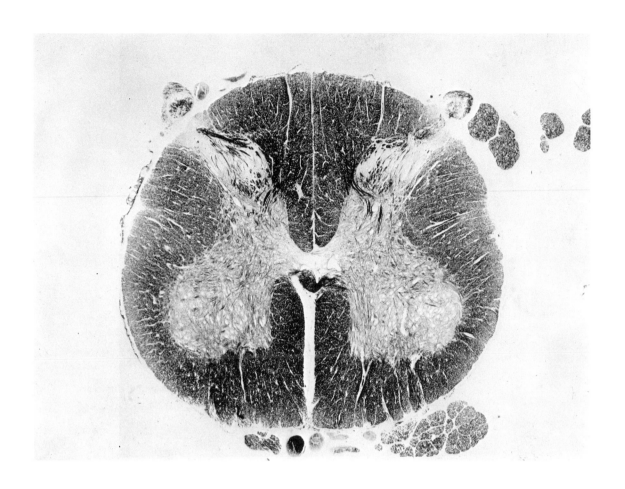

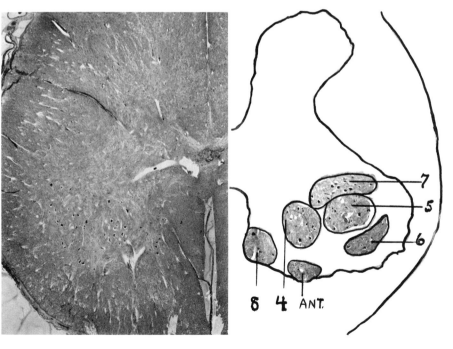

Fourth lumbar segment

7

5

6

8 4 ANT.

113

Fifth Lumbar Segment

Weigert Preparation

The anterior horn and its lateral projection have become more bulbous, with the antero- and posterolateral cell columns occupying the anterior bulge. The considerably broadened posterior horn has acquired greatly increased volume.

Nerve Cells

Column 8 is still seen in the rostral end of this segment (as indicated), but has disappeared from the caudal end. Column 6 has shifted medially.

The nuclear counts in a .25 mm. block were as follows:

Group	Column	Left	Right
Medial	8	59	49
Central	7	80	77
Anterolateral	4	—	—
Posterolateral	5	82	55
	6	77	52

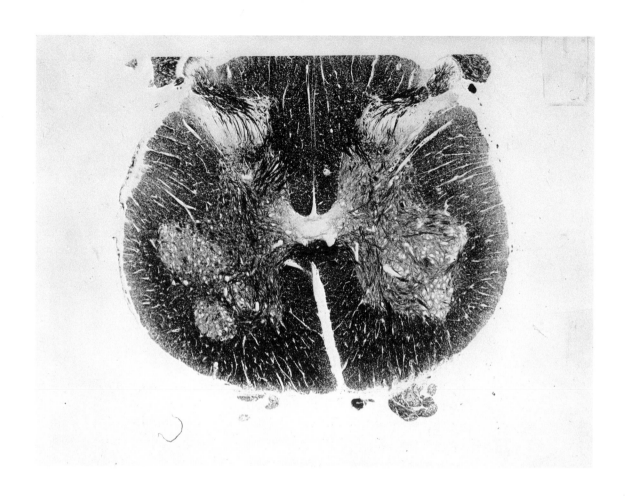

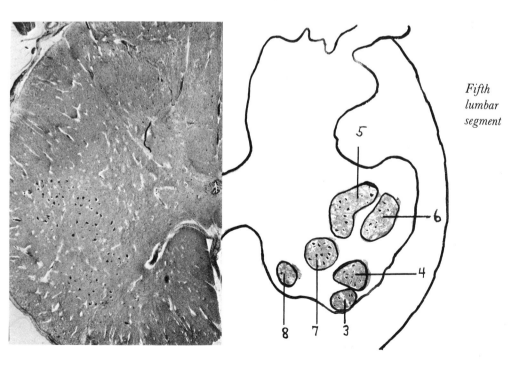

*Fifth
lumbar
segment*

5

6

8 7 3

4

115

First Sacral Segment

Weigert Preparation

The relatively smooth curve forming the medial and anterior boundary of the anterior horn is due to the absence of an anteromedial column. The notch on the lateral border dividing the anterior from the posterior column is still present but is slightly less conspicuous than in more rostral sections. The substantia gelatinosa forms a bulge beyond the neck of the posterior horn.

Nerve Cells

With the disappearance of the group, all the cell columns extend along the lateral bulges of the anterior horn.

The nuclear counts in a .25 mm. block were as follows:

Group	Column	Left	Right
Central	7	111	88
Anterolateral	4	69	65
	3	48	53
Posterolateral	5	85	75
	6	100	55

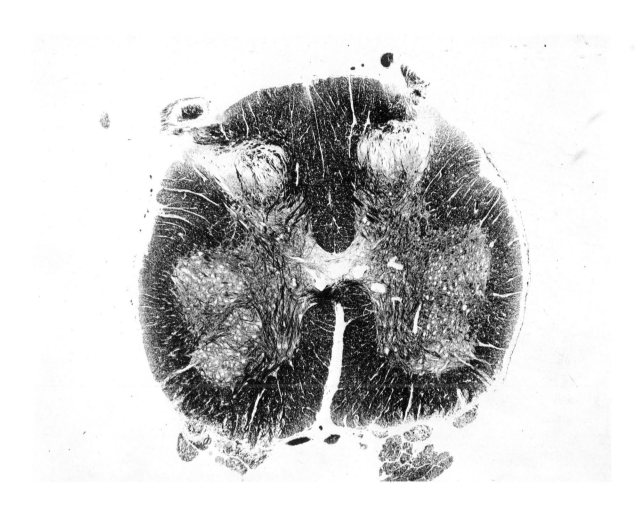

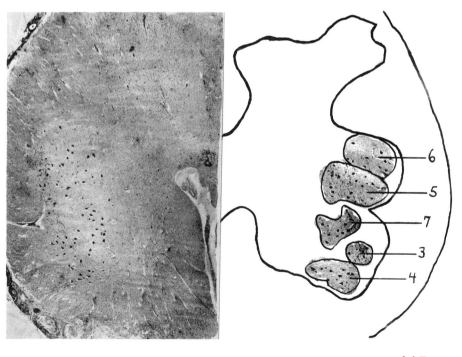

*First
sacral
segment*

6

5

7

3

4

117

Second Sacral Segment

Weigert Preparation

The macroscopic configuration is fairly consistent throughout this segment as seen in the Weigert stain, but the cell picture depends to a certain extent upon how far rostrally or caudally the block has been transected, for the cell columns at this level begin and end abruptly. The bulky gelatinous substance and the depth of the posterior commissure characterize the posterior part of the cord.

Nerve Cells

The medial group is still absent, and the lateral columns lie in a row in the lateral projection of the anterior horn. Column 7, which is composed of at least two parts, has been treated as one column.

The nuclear counts in a .25 mm. block were as follows:

Group	Column	Left	Right
Central	7	96	145
Anterolateral	4	38	49
	3	25	39
Posterolateral	5	37	51
Post-posterolateral	2	64	66

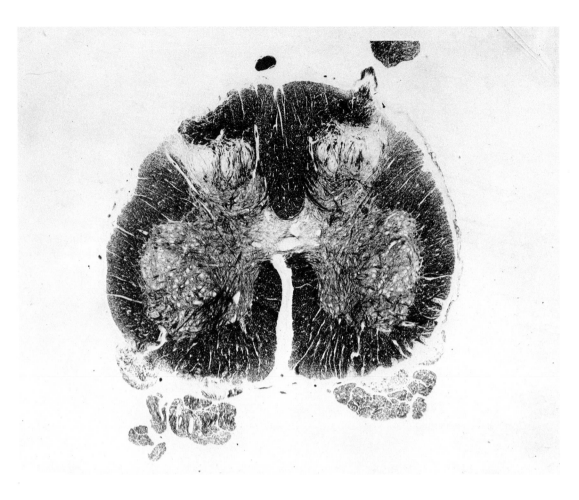

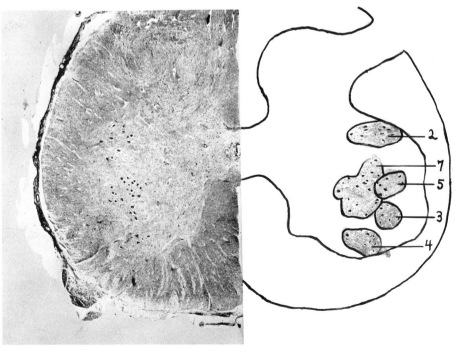

Second sacral segment

119

Third Sacral Segment

Weigert Preparation

The cord is now conspicuously reduced in size, with relatively little white matter in proportion to gray. The most distinguishing mark of the gray matter is the short, broad appearance of the posterior horns. The anterior horns once again have nearly parallel medial edges.

Nerve Cells

The medial group has reappeared, now as column 1, and it is flanked laterally by a subdivision of column 1 from more rostral or caudal regions. In the lateral projection the constituent parts of column 2 are grouped together.

The nuclear counts in a .25 mm. block were as follows:

Group	Column	Left	Right
Medial	1	38	34
Post-posterolateral	2	103	112

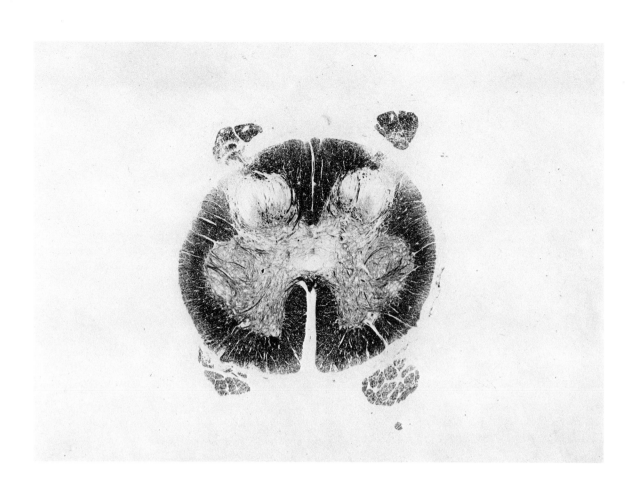

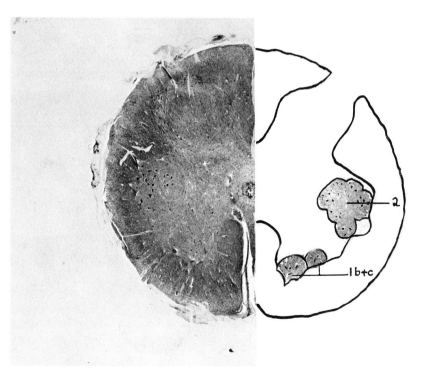

Third
sacral
segment

2

1b+c

Fourth Sacral Segment

Weigert Preparation

In this segment the anterior horns have no lateral projections. The posterior horns are short and broad and in volume appear to exceed the anterior horns.

Nerve Cells

There are no cells in the anterior horn except those of the medial group. The nuclear counts in a .25 mm. block were as follows:

Group	Column	Left	Right
Medial	1	13	20

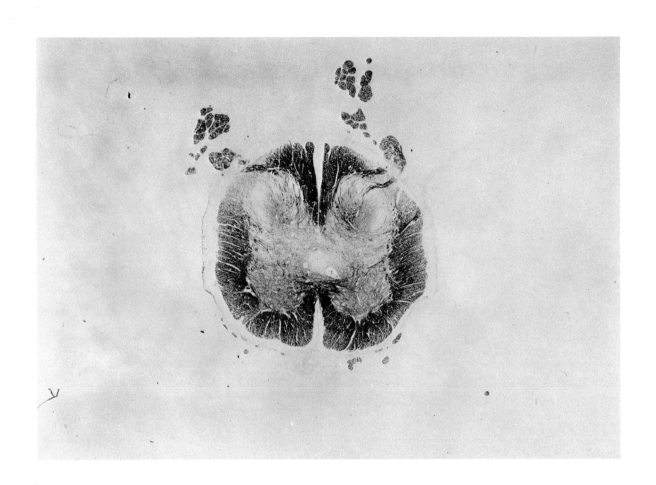

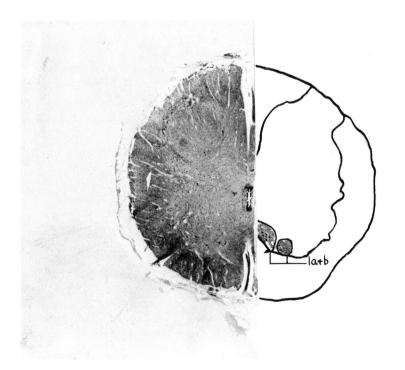

1a+b

*Fourth
sacral
segment*

123

Fifth Sacral Segment

Weigert Preparation

This section has the characteristic anterior and posterior horn appearance seen consistently in more rostral segments and so may still be considered a segment in its own right, especially since a few motor cells are present at its rostral end. The posterior horn is bulbous and larger than the anterior horn.

Nerve Cells

No motor cells are present in the section illustrated.

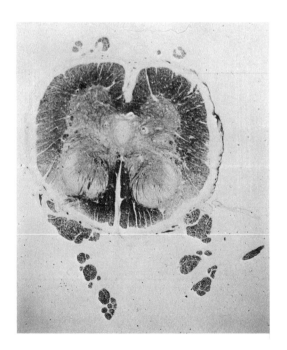